A Guide to
The Oriental Institute
Museum

Published with a Grant from The
The University of Chicago

D1211427

A Guide To The Oriental Institute Museum

THE ORIENTAL
INSTITUTE

THE UNIVERSITY
OF CHICAGO
1982

1 EGYPT   Reconstructed burial of a woman.
Predynastic Period
Naqada II (Gerzean) Period
about 3400 B.C.

human remains, Naga ed-Deir   grave goods, Naqada

Library of Congress Catalogue Card Number 82–81701
International Standard Book Number 0–918986–35–4
© 1982 by The Oriental Institute Museum
The University of Chicago

Designed by Cynthia Susmilch

Printed by The University of Chicago Printing Department

Contents

General Information vii

Foreword
    ROBERT McC. ADAMS, *Director* ix

Preface
    JOHN CARSWELL, *Curator* xi

Introduction 1

THE GALLERY GUIDE

    The Prehistory of the Near East 5

    Egypt 9

    Assyria, Anatolia, and Syria 41

    Mesopotamia 65

    Iran 89

    Palestine and the Islamic Period 111

Chronological Chart 132

Special Exhibitions 135

Oriental Institute Membership 137

Map of the Near East 139

VISIT THE **ORIENTAL INSTITUTE** AT THE

UNIVERSITY OF CHICAGO

SEE THE **FAMOUS CHAPEL AND INTERNATIONAL HOUSE**

HEAR THE • **CARILLON & CHIMES** 5:30 PM • DAILY

AND ORGAN RECITAL • 7 PM DAILY

WALK AROUND •• **THE QUADRANGLES**

ATTEND THE •• **IMPORTANT LECTURES**

General Information

THE ORIENTAL INSTITUTE MUSEUM is located at 58th Street and University Avenue, on the campus of the University of Chicago. It is open from 10:00 a.m. to 4:00 p.m. from Tuesday to Saturday, and from 12:00 to 4:00 p.m. on Sundays. It is closed on Mondays and holidays. The Museum is served by the southern route of the CTA Culture Bus on Sundays during the summer months; for details, phone 664-7200. For general information about the Museum and special exhibitions and lectures, phone 753-2475 during office hours. Permission to photograph objects on display must be obtained from the Museum Office; the use of flash is forbidden.

The Museum maintains its own shop, called The Suq, which is open during Museum hours and which stocks a wide variety of books and merchandise associated with the Near East. For information about The Suq, phone 753-2468/2484.

Oriental Institute publications are obtainable from the Publications Office, 753-2484; photographs of objects in the collection are available from the Archives, 753-2475; for Museum Tours and reservations, phone 753-2475/2485. Volunteer Guides are usually on duty in the Museum itself for individual tours. For details of the Museum Education program, particularly for schools, phone the Educational Coordinator, 753-2573.

2   A vintage Oriental Institute poster in the Art Deco style from the 1930's emphasized the cultural opportunities at the University of Chicago.

3   The "new" Oriental Institute building at the time of its opening in 1931, from the northwest.

Foreword

THE ORIENTAL INSTITUTE, a center of scholarly research within the University of Chicago, is devoted exclusively to the ancient Near East. For more than sixty years it has played a leading part in the study of the world's earliest, longest-lived civilizations and their antecedents. Included in its faculty and professional staff, numbering nearly thirty, are historians, archaeologists, specialists in more than twenty ancient languages, and laboratory scientists engaged in field studies as well as conservation. Their common efforts to advance the frontiers of scholarship are focused on the recovery, recording, interpretation, and ultimately publication of growing bodies of textual, archaeological, and environmental data that largely derive from their own field research. Through the University's College and its graduate departments of Near Eastern Languages and Civilizations, Anthropology, Linguistics, and Geography, the faculty of the Institute also engages in general education as well as in the advanced training of scholars.

The Oriental Institute's Museum is an expression of both its scholarly commitments and its broad concern for public education and outreach. Materials brought home from the field must be preserved for future studies that will pursue new questions with as yet unanticipated methods. At the same time, those collections of material offer original testimony on more general themes that can be apprehended by everyone. Different groups of objects in the Museum may help you, for example, to form your own impressions of some of the decisive turning-points in the human career—the transition from hunting and food collecting to agriculture, the birth of urban civilization and literacy, the origins of several of the world's great religions, and the gathering tides of technological and scientific discovery. Or individual objects may stand forth independently, across space and time, as symbols of shared hopes, efforts, insights, shortcomings, and tragedies. We believe you will find this guidebook instructive on many points, but its larger purpose is to assist you in forming your own, highly personal links with the human past.

ROBERT McC. ADAMS
Director

4   Dr. James Henry Breasted at his desk in the Haskell Oriental Museum, about 1926.

Preface

THE MUSEUM OF THE ORIENTAL INSTITUTE performs a dual role: while it is primarily a study collection, closely connected with the work of the Institute as a research organization, it is also a source of information for the public at large. Just as the Oriental Institute is unique in its focus on the study of the origins of civilization in the ancient Near East, the Museum houses an unparalleled collection of antiquities, on which much of this research is based. What gives the collection its special importance is that much of the material is of known provenance. Unlike many more widely-known museum collections where the objects were acquired by purchase, the majority of the artifacts in the Oriental Institute Museum were found as a result of the Institute's own excavations. This known provenance, and the records of the discovery of the objects held in the Institute's archives, add immeasurably to their scientific value. This is not to deny that the objects have a powerful aesthetic appeal apart from their archaeological context. Like all works of art, many of the pieces on display have an appeal to a wide variety of visitors, on many different levels of interest.

During the sixty years that the Oriental Institute has been working in the field, more than 80,000 artifacts have been brought back to Chicago, for study and publication, and it is the function of the Museum to conserve this material. With such a mass of material only a fraction can be on display at any given time, but since its inception the Oriental Institute has always made available to the general public a representative selection of some of its finest objects. The Museum was originally housed in Haskell Hall at the University of Chicago. It was moved to its present location in 1931, when the new Oriental Institute was opened on December 5th of that year by its lifelong patron, John D. Rockefeller, Jr. Rockefeller was a friend and ardent supporter of the Institute's founder, James Henry Breasted, and the new building was the direct result of a journey they made together to the Near East in 1929, visiting the sites where Institute work was in progress.

JOHN CARSWELL
Curator

4

3,5   The new Oriental Institute and Museum was designed by the New York firm of Mayers, Murray, and Phillips, and is a handsome structure of architectural interest in its own right, combining European and Near Eastern motifs and providing a sympathetic setting for the wide variety of material on display. Besides the exhibition galleries, which are open free of charge to the general public, there are also facilities for the preservation, conservation, and recording of material in the basement, and study areas for scholars and students. As the number of objects in the collection far exceeds available display space, the situation is remedied by temporary exhibits of selected groups of material. Loan exhibitions, both to and from other institutions in the United States and abroad, have become an increasingly important feature in recent years, helping to generate interest in the Oriental Institute's world-famous collection and in the whole field of Near Eastern civilization and history.

In order to interpret the collection and make sure that visitors derive maximum satisfaction from their experience, the Museum maintains a vigorous Volunteer Program, which is responsible for the training of volunteer guides for both individual and group tours. Volunteers also help in many other backstage aspects of the Museum operation. Recently, special kits for schoolchildren and their teachers, which can be obtained in advance of planned group visits, have been devised under the supervision of the Educational Coordinator. In addition, the Oriental Institute has an active Membership Program, with over two thousand members, details of which may be found at the end of this Guide.

The present Guide to the Oriental Institute Museum was written by Leon Marfoe, and edited by Peter T. Daniels and Valerie M. Fargo. All the Museum staff have been involved in its production in one way or another, and valuable advice has been given by Bruce Williams, Peggy Grant, Joan Barghusen, Samuel Wolff, John Larson, and Joseph Greene; special thanks are due to Myrna Simon, the Museum Secretary, for typing the final draft of the manuscript.

The illustrations were drawn by Mark Frueh. Many of the photographs were specially taken by Jean Grant, ably aided by her volunteer assistant, Joseph

Denov. Material for the map was compiled by Bruce Verhaaren. The Guide was designed by Cynthia Susmilch and produced by the Printing Department of The University of Chicago.

Finally, a word about the Guide itself. It is, in part, a permanent reference. At the same time, it is designed to be used by visitors to the Museum, to orient them to the various parts of the collection, and to provide the necessary historical background. Each section is in two parts, a historical narrative followed by a detailed description of what is on display. But museums can never be static, and with changing exhibits the actual location of objects referred to in the text may alter in the future, a factor to be taken into account by anyone using the Guide. What we hope the Guide will do is to give some idea of the scope and richness of the collection, and an insight into the relationship between the objects on display and the activities of one of the world's leading research institutions for the study of the past.

5 "East Meets West," the relief sculpture decorating the tympanum above the main entrance of the Oriental Institute building, designed by Ulric W. Ellerhusen.

Introduction

THE NEAR EAST, a broad geographical zone encompassing the modern countries of Egypt, Syria, Turkey, Lebanon, Jordan, Israel, Iraq, Iran, and the countries of the Arabian peninsula, may not have been the sole center of the civilizations of the ancient world, but it was certainly the earliest. By the time other civilizations had arisen in the Indus Valley and China, the Andes and MesoAmerica, Near Eastern influence had spread into the adjacent areas of the Sudan and Ethiopia, North Africa, Cyprus, the eastern Mediterranean and Aegean, and ultimately to Europe in the West and Afghanistan and India in the East. By the early centuries of the Christian era the impact of the Near East was felt as far as China and, further stimulated by the advent of Islam, has continued its influence in the East. The Near Eastern civilizations, so long etched into the record of human achievement and endeavor, serve as a reference point for the whole scope of humane and scientific inquiry into the past.

The constituents of ancient Near Eastern civilization are in fact a heterogeneous group of cultures that had their roots in a still imperfectly known prehistoric past several million years old, and that crystallized into an urban society of literate states and empires around 3000 B.C. Originating in the twin foci of the Nile Valley in Egypt and the Tigris/Euphrates floodplain of Mesopotamia, in a remarkably short period of time a series of parallel cultures spread throughout Iran, Syria/Palestine, and Turkey that lasted until the rise of the Greco-Roman world. Numbered among the achievements of these diverse cultures—of which those of Egypt, Mesopotamia, and the Biblical lands are certainly the best known—were the first attempts at food production, the construction of cities, the invention of writing and the alphabet, the creation of monumental works of architecture and art, and, perhaps the most enduring legacy of all, the monotheistic religions still part of our lives today.

The peoples of the ancient Near East inhabited a landscape as varied as their civilizations. In its broadest aspect five elements stand out prominently: a long northern ridge of mountains curving in an arc from Palestine through Turkey into Iran; highland plateaus and salty depressions beyond this arc in Turkey and Iran; a broad strip of arable land on the inner arc of the mountains (aptly named by James Henry Breasted the "Fertile Crescent"); an area of steppe and desert within the Fertile Crescent extending from northern Syria to southern Arabia; and the great river valleys of the Nile and the Euphrates running their courses through these desert areas.

Each distinctive region harbored a unique civilization. On the floodplains the civilizations of ancient Egypt, Assyria, and Babylonia are perhaps the best known. But on the highland plateaus of Turkey and Iran arose the Hittites and the Persians, and on the spiny ridges of the Fertile Crescent to the west emerged the Phoenicians, Canaanites, and Israelites. These ancient roots of humanity, so distant in time but so close in import today, form one of the major branches of scientific research in the area.

The Oriental Institute has as its purpose the concentrated study of the human past in the Near East, and since 1919 has carried out researches drawing on a unique combination of specialists in many fields. These projects have been pursued along two principal lines of inquiry, archaeology and philology, investigating respectively the material and written legacy of the past. Whether on horseback or camel, by jeep or airplane, archaeologists have undertaken over thirty expeditions throughout the Near East. In pre-war years the large-scale projects were centered on six main regions of the Near East, but since then the scope has widened to include ancient Carthage in Tunisia, North Yemen, and the Egyptian/Islamic port of Quseir on the Red Sea. It has maintained its interest in Iran, in the Protoliterate city of Chogha Mish; in Nippur, etc., in Iraq; in the earliest villages of the Fertile Crescent at Çayönü in eastern Turkey; in the investigation of ancient Mesopotamian water systems and settlement patterns; and in the monumental work of the Epigraphic Survey based at Chicago House in Luxor, Egypt.

In these days of fragile academic budgets and increased dependence on Federal and private subsidies, ambitious archaeological projects have of necessity been tempered by harsh realities, and in this restricted economic climate both the projects and the research techniques to carry them out have been sharply re-defined to establish priorities and to utilize a wide variety of analytical techniques.

The second main task of the Oriental Institute has been the recording, decipherment, and interpretation of ancient written records: before the task of historical reconstruction can begin, their languages demand detailed comprehension. One of the major achievements of the Institute has been the compilation of dictionaries in various of these languages, fundamental tools for research. The pride of place must be given to the Assyrian Dictionary, which during more than half a century has laid down the foundation for all work in Assyriology. Other dictionary projects include Hittite, demotic Egyptian, Sumerian, and Oromo, the principal modern Cushitic language of Ethiopia. Building on these massive philological efforts, the guiding principle of the Oriental Institute continues to be the historical reconstruction of the past. The long-range guidelines and the programs initiated by our founder, James Henry Breasted, are still relevant, and among the tangible evidence of these efforts are the unique collections of the Oriental Institute Museum.

The Prehistory of the Near East

IN THE NEAR EAST, writing and the recording of history began around 3000 B.C. Our ancestors, however, were by this time long-term residents of the area. The vast span of time from the first appearance of man to the first writing is called prehistory.

Different techniques of making implements out of flint materials are the primary information used in identifying and dating the early presence of the human genus. In general, the tools of the Lower and Middle Paleolithic (or the Early and Middle Old Stone Age, about three million to 40,000 years ago) were made by shaping the cores of flint nodules to form bifaces. The earliest evidence of tool-making in the Near East comes from Ubeidiya, just south of the Sea of Galilee in Palestine. There, tools similar to those found by L. S. B. Leakey at Olduvai Gorge in Africa have been found. But the earliest human remains in the Near East are much later, and come from Mount Carmel in Palestine and Shanidar in Iraq. Dated to about 50,000–40,000 years ago, these remains are of the Neanderthal variety, a close predecessor of modern man.

Modern man comes slightly later, and is associated with a new tool tradition in which blade implements are made from the flakes rather than the cores of flint nodules. At this time, the Upper Paleolithic (or the Late Old Stone Age, about 40,000 to 17,000 years ago), the principal habitations were still in large caves. The best examples of this period are to be found in cave deposits in Lebanon (Ksar Akil) and Palestine (Tabun), although other remains have also been found in Syria (Yabrud) and Iraq (Shanidar). These indicate that although the principal methods of obtaining food were still in the "hunting-collecting" stage, open-air sites may have been used for such temporary activities as butchering wild game that would have been difficult to carry back home intact.

As the last Ice Age drew to a close around 15,000 to 10,000 years ago, a new tool industry appeared, characterized by small flint blades combined to form a single cutting edge. These new tools, microliths, are the hallmark of the Mesolithic period (or Middle Stone Age, about 17,000 to 8000 B.C.). This new era also brings some other major changes. The first, already begun at the end of the Upper Paleolithic, was the gradual expansion of the hunter-collector's diet to include a wide range of smaller food sources. These included game, fish, crabs, turtles, snails, fowl, mussels, wild grain, and nuts. The second change was the transition from cave dwelling to settled villages. In these early villages, some of which are very large, a vastly expanded repertoire of tools and utensils is used in everyday life. Thus we find items such as fishhooks and harpoons made of bone, large stone mortars and primitive grinders, imported shells from distant places, and even works of art.

The entire period at the end of the last Ice Age is now customarily regarded as a major turning point in the development of modern society, representing the shift from food collection to food production. The agricultural revolution set the stage for changes in society, culture, and politics that ultimately gave birth to the first cities and states, and the civilizations of the Near East. Hence, the next period, commonly called the Neolithic (or New Stone Age, about 8000 to 4000 B.C.), is better characterized not by its tools but by the first definite signs that the domestication of wild plants and animals, agriculture and animal husbandry, had taken place.

Certainly the most important remains are those of the newly domesticated plants and animals. Both the identification and study of the evolution of the various plant and animal remains are specialized topics; but it is precisely in areas of interdisciplinary research like these that archaeology contributes to an otherwise invisible history. From about 7000 B.C. down to around 2500 B.C. the rollcall of plants and animals newly domesticated is most impressive. First came early forms of the principal cereals, two-row barley, emmer wheat, and einkorn wheat. Along with these plants, a number of animals are also known: the domesticated dog, sheep, and goat, the latter pair difficult to tell apart except for their horns.

Shortly after, the more developed species of six-row barley and bread wheat appear. At this point, if not earlier, domesticated cattle and probably pigs join the menagerie. From about 5000 B.C. onward, flax, which can be used for oil as well as woven cloth, was introduced, and the olive was cultivated primarily for its oil. Both developments are significant because these new crops are frequently produced in quantities too large for family consumption, and therefore may have been used for trade. In any case the next two thousand years seem to represent a breakthrough in the farming of fruits and similar "cash" crops. By about 2000 B.C., an increasing number of such crops as the grape and date palm are known. As a result, the foundations of modern economy were established. The most remarkable aspect of this history, however, is that it is traced through such methods as the measurement of bone and seed sizes, and that isolated facts such as the gradual appearance of wool on domesticated sheep only emerge from such painstaking studies.

Along with these revolutionary changes, other facets of prehistoric life unfold at a dramatic pace. Farming village communities become a permanent feature of the landscape. Even in this early period, some of these settlements are very large and impressive, and have sophisticated architecture. A round tower and fortification wall at Jericho, in Palestine, is the first of its kind. In Turkey, elaborate buildings are found at Çayönü, and a large complex of rooms with murals and elaborate cultic fixtures has been excavated at Çatal Hüyük. During this period, pottery also gradually came into use around 6000 B.C., and elaborate burials became common, with some burial practices reflecting new attitudes toward death: there is reason to believe that burials were accompanied by ritual behavior. Trade with distant places, particularly in obsidian and later in copper, became more frequent. A gradual change in kinds of stone tools also reflects changes in the daily occupations of people; hunting weapons decline while woodworking and harvesting tools predominate.

By the Chalcolithic period (literally "Copper" Stone Age), around 5000 B.C., the stage was set for new levels in the complexity of human society and in its achievements. The appearance of leaders was the forerunner of kings and kingdoms. The building of small shrines heralded the coming of temples and priests. And the introduction of copperworking, gold, and silver laid the foundations not only for a new technology, but also for the use of money. Civilization was about to reach a new threshold.

Egypt

EGYPT was the focus of an enduring cultural development that was more distinctive and continuous
than that of her nearest rival, Mesopotamia. Despite
occasional conquests by her neighbors, the three
thousand years of Pharaonic Egyptian history are a
tapestry of monuments, literature, art, and politics
(with a single theme: the uniqueness of the "Black
Land"). In part, this unity and uniqueness of the
Egyptian people and their culture, and their ambitions, achievements, victories, and defeats arose
from a singular geography. Ancient Egypt, properly
speaking, is a long narrow trough of black earth—
never more than ten or twenty miles wide—extending some seven hundred miles from Elephantine to
the Mediterranean Sea, and emptying into the broad,
marshy stretches of the Delta. On either side of this
trough, vast expanses of red sandstone deserts and
cliffs, the "Red Land," guaranteed the splendid iso-
lation of this valley by permitting access by only a
limited number of routes. The Nile was the unifying
feature of the country, and whether south to Nubia,
west to Libya, east to the Red Sea and the Sinai, or
north across the Mediterranean, travel to and from
Egypt was arduous, lengthy, and costly. Internally,
too, other features of her geography may in part have
been responsible for the motives and causes behind
the characteristic rise and fall of Egyptian civilization. A long chain of flood basins in Upper Egypt
(the Valley) and Lower Egypt (the Delta) divided the
land into natural provinces that persistently sought
independence during times of distress. At such
times, frequent complaints of widespread famine are
sometimes blamed on a series of abnormally high
and low floods. In this respect, the natural annual
flooding of the Nile River was the dominating
feature—whether good or bad—of valley life because
seasonal and long-term changes in its flow could
mark the difference between poverty and plenty. But
even in times of plenty, the lack of certain natural
resources—particularly wood and copper—would
lead Egypt to a pattern of periodic, though tempo-

HISTORICAL VIEW

rary, imperial conquests abroad. The Nile was thus both boon and burden.

The early development of prehistoric cultures in Egypt may have gotten off to a slow start by comparison with her neighbors in Western Asia. The earliest remains of human settlement in the Predynastic period are not much earlier than about 5000 B.C., and appear in two different areas. In the north, three poorly understood villages at Fayum, Merimde, and Maadi are virtually all that is known up to about 3000 B.C. In Middle Egypt, excavations at cemeteries suggest that a separate culture, the Badarian, emerged around Abydos, located mainly near the desert margins just beyond the Valley floor. These graves usually contained a distinctive pottery, "Black-topped" ware, simple slate palettes, and ivory objects. Slightly later, in the Amratian period (ca. 4000 B.C.), this culture expanded toward the north and south and onto the Valley floor. Grave goods now included (besides new shapes of "Black-topped" ware) new kinds of pottery, stone vessels, slate palettes, sculptured terra cotta figurines, and imported copper. Gradually, an increasing sophistication in daily life, in thoughts on the afterlife, and in the self-consciousness reflected in personal decoration developed into the last phase of Predynastic culture, the Gerzean (Naqada II) period (after 4000 B.C. to ca. 3100 B.C.). New pottery decorated with red-painted human figures, boats, and birds replaced "Black-topped" ware; slate palettes were carved into animal forms; stone vessels became more common and elaborate; flint knives became beautifully flaked; and influences from Mesopotamia and Palestine, reflected in stone carving, cylinder seals, pottery, copper, and other imports, became commonplace.

Dramatic events must have taken place near the end of the Gerzean period. Perhaps influenced in some way by relations with Nubia, Mesopotamia, and Palestine, local kings arose in Upper and Lower Egypt, and by 3150 B.C. the spread of the Gerzean culture northward gives an indication that the unification of Egypt was underway. In any case, the white crown of Upper Egypt and the red crown of Lower Egypt were combined into one crown under Narmer, the last of the Predynastic kings of Egypt. With this act, Egypt was established as a world power.

What unfolded in the following Archaic period (Dynasties I–III, ca. 3100–2680 B.C.) then set the stage for the full flowering of Egyptian culture. Gerzean-tradition slate palettes, stone vessels, pottery, and ceremonial maceheads continued in representational form and became more stylized. But certainly the dominating feature of Archaic Egypt was the evolution of burial customs from the use of a simple mastaba to multi-stepped platforms, and from simple houses for the dead to carefully maintained funerary cults. Influenced in part by Mesopotamian brick architecture, the development of royal tombs from the niched, bench-like "mastabas" at Saqqara (and probably Abydos) to the mighty Stepped Pyramid of Djoser (Dynasty III) at Saqqara is a continuous tradition of increasing splendor, opulence, and power. From inscriptions found near these tombs, we get an idea of the gradual changes in writing, of the identification of kings with the god Horus (designated by a hawk), and perhaps too of a political crisis in the later Second Dynasty.

The Archaic prelude led directly to the tremendous achievements of the Old Kingdom (Dynasties IV–VI, ca. 2680–2300 B.C.), the great pyramid age of Egypt that was to establish a cultural continuity lasting through the succeeding centuries. In art, tomb paintings and sculpture in the round and in relief display the development of conventions which were to be followed for three thousand years. In funerary arrangements, statues of the tomb owners and the general concepts of the afterlife are represented for the first time. Religious texts, such as the Pyramid texts (magical spells written only in royal tombs), and religious practices appeared that were prototypes for subsequent eras. The Egyptians' attitude of superiority toward Nubians, Libyans, and Asiatics, manifest in their policies of trade and conquest, recurs time and again.

As seen in the majestic tombs for the kings of Egypt and the more modest mastabas of the courtiers and nobility, the Old Kingdom is also the story of the first cycle of rise and fall in Egyptian history. The monumental size of the great pyramids of Giza evidences the perception of the king as not only a god, but the dominant god of the state. But by the latter part of Dynasty IV, subtle changes in the king's titles and in the grandeur of his tomb indicate a relative weakening of this idea. The erection of solar temples and the decreased size of the pyramids of the Fifth and Sixth Dynasties may reflect a shift of emphasis from the king as god to the king as the son of a god, Re. Also indicative of this rise and decline in royal status are the tombs of the nobility. In the Fourth Dynasty, these were placed around the king's tomb. But as time passed, these mastabas became more elaborate, displaying personal cults, and by the late Sixth Dynasty the tombs of provincial officials were to be found in their home provinces. With writing more formalized, several kinds of literature also appear, and they too are a record of royal rise and fall. From the Fourth Dynasty on, biographies of tomb owners are written on the walls of the tombs, and by the Sixth Dynasty this important literary genre had developed into a long and increasingly immodest appraisal of the owner's life. They parallel the appearance of another kind of literature, wisdom sayings with advice stressing the virtues necessary to direct a life and career in its proper course. Both kinds of literature begin to depict the nobles as self-sufficient, egotistic, and individualistic men of power increasingly independent of the king. By the late Sixth Dynasty, kingship was less a fact than fiction.

For many possible reasons, the breakup of central authority at the end of the Old Kingdom led to a relatively short period of rival local dynasties and kingdoms, the First Intermediate Period (Dynasties VII to early XI, ca. 2250–2040 B.C.). In this era after the passing of the "Golden Age," numerous developments reflected the impact of political realities upon the Egyptians' concept of their world. In tomb furnishings, for instance, depictions of daily life (including models of daily activities), letters to the dead, and boat models accompanied the tomb owner into the netherworld. The tombs themselves were cut deeper underground and no longer followed a single model. The gradual democratization of funerary beliefs culminated in the Coffin texts which derived from the royal Pyramid texts and made the afterlife accessible to the common people. In wisdom literature, new texts dominated by pessimism and insecurity appeared. Texts, tales, and royal propaganda were written in a new form of the Egyptian language that became a model for later generations. Art became more careless and diverged more and more from the standards of the Old Kingdom. The common "hieratic" script appeared and displays significant differences that had emerged between everyday usage and the official monumental inscriptions. Out of this diversity, a national consensus only gradually reappeared with the reunification of the Nile valley under the Eleventh Dynasty of Thebes. The legacy of past traumas, however, was never to be forgotten.

The national consensus was forged by the kings of the Middle Kingdom (Dynasties XI–XIII, ca. 2040–1720 B.C.), the period in which many of the artistic standards of the Old Kingdom were restored by the reigning dynasty, and in which Egyptian literature became a model for later generations. It is the remains of this literature, in the form of folktales and wisdom writings, along with the more abundant records and accounts, that shed light on a humanizing trend in the depiction of kings. Otherwise, the main thrust of the new national policy may have been an attempt to re-establish control over the local provinces or "Nomes." A new capital was established at Itjt-tawy, near Memphis, although the home of the new dynasty, Thebes, remained the center of the growing cult of Amun. From this capital, the Twelfth Dynasty reorganized the old provinces and undertook an aggressive military expansion and fortification program against a vigorous population in Nubia, the C-Group people. In Western Asia, contacts were re-established with old centers like Byblos, and a network of diplomacy and trade accompanied these contacts. The building of royal tombs resumed with the erection of pyramids following the earlier traditions. But in the provinces, extremely elaborate local tombs, such as at Qau and Beni Hasan, seem to attest to the presence of separatist tendencies in that they usurp the symbols of royalty on their decorations.

It is therefore not too surprising that a fairly rapid decline in political authority occurred soon after the Thirteenth Dynasty took power, and ushered in the Second Intermediate Period (Dynasties XIV–XVII, ca. 1720–1570 B.C.). Due only in part to local ambitions, and perhaps more to the extension of contacts with Western Asia, a gradual immigration of Asiatics into the Delta resulted in a takeover of the northeast Delta by Asiatic rulers called the Hyksos. Remembered in later tradition as hated foreign usurpers, the Hyksos' Fifteenth Dynasty ousted the Thirteenth Dynasty from Itjt-tawy. Other parts of Egypt were divided under the control of separate dynasties. The Seventeenth Dynasty held Thebes, while part of the Delta was initially held by the Fourteenth Dynasty, who were succeeded by a number of petty princes (the Sixteenth Dynasty). Over a short span of time, about a century, the Hyksos became rapidly acculturated to Egyptian customs, and in return Asiatic innovations were introduced into Egypt. But this second cycle of decline ended with yet another unification, the reconquest of the Nile valley by Seqenenre Tao and Kamose of the Theban Seventeenth Dynasty.

The memory of recent foreign domination by the Hyksos was the motive for the policies of the Egyptian New Kingdom (Dynasties XVIII–XIX, ca. 1570–1070 B.C.). The kings of this period led Egypt to a new age of imperialism and world influence, great building programs, artistic and literary achievements, and, ultimately, changes in Egyptian society. After they consolidated their hold on a reunified Egypt, there was a dramatic expansion of military might into Nubia and Western Asia. In Nubia, a local population was substantially assimilated into a network of forts and temples. In Syria-Palestine, campaigns by Ahmose I, Thutmosis I, the great Thutmosis III, and Amenhotep II extended Egyptian domination as far as Lebanon and Syria. There, they rapidly came into contact with the other emerging powers of the ancient Near East: the Hittites, the Mitannians, the Assyrians, and the Babylonians. Egyptian influence in Western Asia receded somewhat in the later part of the Eighteenth Dynasty, but under the resurgent Nineteenth Dynasty, Seti I and Ramesses II were able to re-establish control of some of Egypt's former possessions. Apart from the exchange of Egyptian and foreign goods between these two areas, vivid portrayals of Egypt's exploits are depicted on monumental reliefs such as those decorating the mortuary temples of Ramesses II. Records too of relations with local Asiatic kings and Hittite and Mitannian royalty are seen in the letters found at Amarna, Akhenaton's capital, and on the inscriptions left by the Egyptian kings. Egyptian foreign relations, it seems, left a trail of alliances, wars, betrayals, and diplomacy not unlike those of the modern world.

From their capital in Memphis and their religious center in Thebes, the kings of the New Kingdom undertook a number of construction projects. The most prominent of these projects involved the necropolis and temples in the Theban area, where the royal tombs, mortuary temples, and civil temples were constructed in the Valley of the Kings and on the west and east banks of the Nile. To accomplish some of these tasks, a village was built at Deir el-Medina solely to accommodate the workmen and craftsmen necessary for the job. Akhenaton, who espoused the worship of the Aton or sun-disk, also built a new, short-lived, capital at Amarna, while Ramesses II erected numerous temples and monuments in addition to constructing a new capital at Per-Ramesses in the Delta. These new developments in architecture were adorned in a range of flourishing art styles. On temple walls, monumental reliefs documenting the deeds of the kings were introduced under Seti I and his successors. Within the tombs, detailed scenes of daily life decorated the walls, and anthropoid rather than rectangular coffins had come into vogue. Instead of "coffin texts" inscribed on the coffin itself, these spells were now collected into the "Book of the Dead," and instead of wooden models, tomb furniture frequently included small "ushabti's," proxy workmen who were to toil in the netherworld for the tomb owner. Both literature and language evolved, as reflected in changes in speech and script; new literary genres appeared in the form of oracles inscribed on pottery; and a plethora of economic documents shed light on such aspects of the priesthood of Amun in Thebes as the administration of estates. Indeed, there are even documents recording the trial of royal tomb robbers, of harem intrigues surrounding the presumed assassination of Ramesses III, and of workmen's strikes for pay. In this glimpse into the more human aspects of ancient life, the remarkable history of Akhenaton and his dramatic shift from established religions and royal practices, and the short career of the boy king, Tutankhamun, whose premature death led to the end of his dynasty, are vignettes deservedly evoking modern sympathy. The art of the Amarna period, which departs substantially from the otherwise formal tone of monumental art by rendering its subject in naturalistic forms, is distinctive.

Whatever strides were made during the New Kingdom, however, Egypt once again went into decline in the later Nineteenth and Twentieth Dynasties. Invaders from Libya and the Mediterranean (the "Sea Peoples") were among those repulsed by Ramesses III. But the scene depicting this triumph at Medinet Habu gives little hint of the disintegration of the Egyptian empire in Western Asia at this time. Internally too, royal prerogatives were increasingly usurped by the high priests of Amun. The final collapse of the New Kingdom saw the division of the country once again into two halves, ruled from Thebes and Per-Ramesses. With this division, the poorly documented age called the Third Intermediate Period (Dynasties XXI–XXV, ca. 1070–660 B.C.) begins. The history of this period is essentially that of a series of weak dynasties, several of which consisted of foreign rulers. Dynasties XXII, XXIII, and XXIV, for instance, were established by Libyan rulers, while Dynasty XXV was the achievement of Nubian pharaohs. Dynasty XXIV was another period of internal chaos when numerous local kings exercised their sway over different parts of the country. Not until Dynasty XXVI was there a relatively brief span of indigenous rule in Egypt. Thereafter, Egypt was again successfully conquered by the Persians, the Greeks (including the well-known Cleopatra), the Romans, and finally the Moslems. A local dynasty did not emerge again until the Fatimid Caliphate in the ninth century A.D.

GALLERY PLAN

Egypt

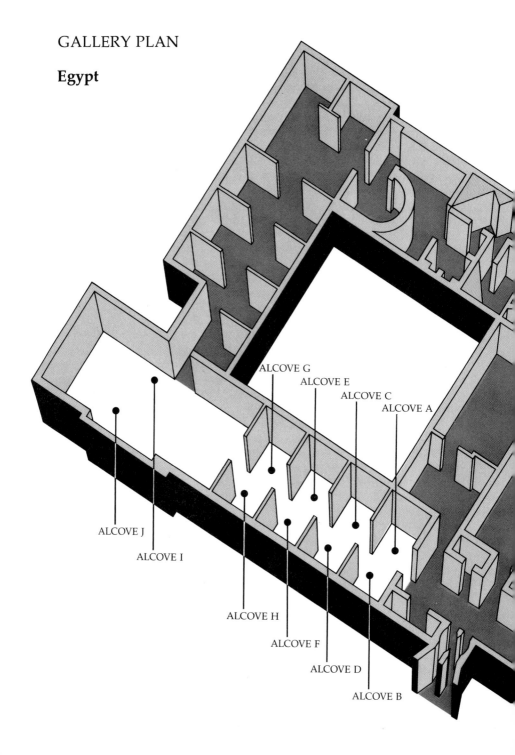

ALCOVE G

ALCOVE E

ALCOVE C

ALCOVE A

ALCOVE J

ALCOVE I

ALCOVE H

ALCOVE F

ALCOVE D

ALCOVE B

GALLERY EXHIBITS

Egypt

The museum's collections form one of the largest and most complete depositories of Egyptian antiquities in the United States. Mostly obtained from purchases, they are particularly representative in their portrayal of ancient Egyptian daily life, but less comprehensive on the political highlights and principal historical figures of Egyptian civilization.

A

I

Alcove A (right side of entrance)

The *Formative Stages of Egyptian Civilization,* the Predynastic and Dynasty I periods, are highlighted in this and the following alcove. The earliest remains, flint tools from various Paleolithic and Neolithic sites, are shown in case A-8. In the center of the alcove is a typical Predynastic burial, in which the crouched body is surrounded by burial offerings. Since most of our knowledge of the Predynastic period comes from cemeteries of such burials, the primary means of dating these burials and sorting them into periods of cultural development is to note the changes in the offerings, a method called "sequence dating" (see chart against back wall). The most important objects for dating are the pottery vessels shown in cases A-1 to A-6, of which the "Black-topped ware" in A-6 and the wavy-handled jars in A-3 are especially significant. The changes in the wavy handle give an idea of how artifacts gradu-

6   Many-oared ship and ostrich(?) in the desert hills; two design elements on a decorated pottery jar.
10758
Predynastic Period
Naqada II (Gerzean) Period
about 3600–3200 B.C.

color plate, opposite:
7 PALESTINE Gaming board; ivory, inlaid with gold.
A 22254
Late Bronze Age II
13th century B.C.
Megiddo
Treasury, near the palace

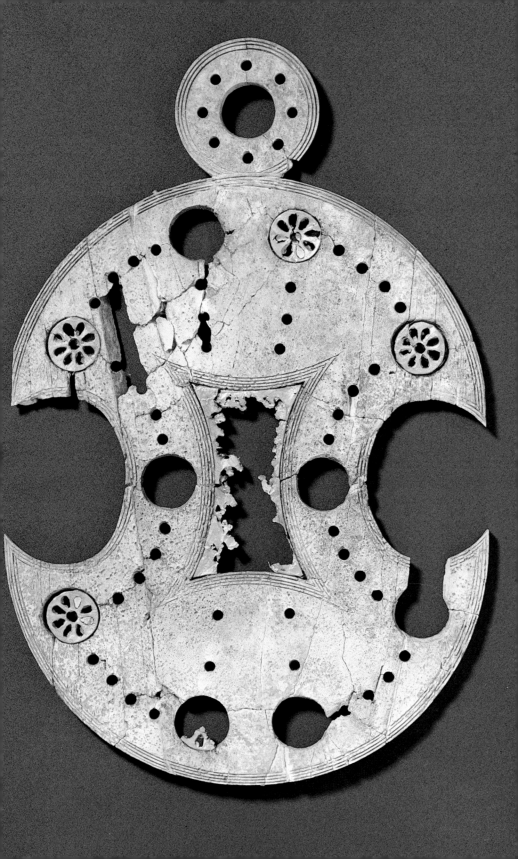

ally change over time and provide us with a dating clue. Whole groups of artifacts from such burials are displayed in A-7, where the series of changes from the Amratian (top shelf) to the Gerzean (middle shelf) and then to Dynasty I (bottom shelf) can be observed. In these early periods, the tomb was already conceived as a "house for eternity," and decorations on tomb walls—such as the replica of a late Gerzean painting hanging over cases A-4 to A-6—preceded the more elaborate painted tombs of later times.

Alcove B (left side of entrance)
The main *Artistic, Technical, and Political Achievements of the Predynastic Periods and Dynasty I* are seen here. In case B-4 are some good examples of slate palettes from this period. These were often placed in tombs along with pebbles for grinding cosmetics and colors (as in the burial in alcove A) should the deceased be required to appear before the gods. By

B

10

9   A rare duck-shaped jar; red breccia.
10859
Predynastic Period
Naqada II (Gerzean) Period
about 3600–3200 B.C.

color plate, opposite:
8   EGYPT   Quail chick, the hieroglyph for the *w*-sound, a sculptor's study or votive plaque; limestone.
18215 (formerly,
Art Institute of Chicago 20.256)
Ptolemaic Period
332–30 B.C.

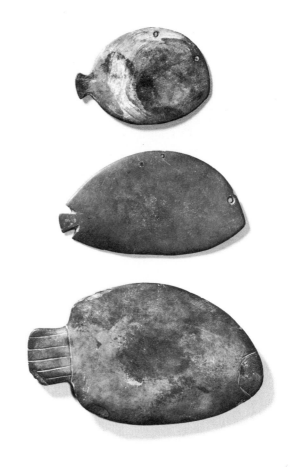

10 Cosmetic palettes
fashioned to resemble
fishes; slate.
5256
11465
873
Predynastic Period
Naqada I-II (late Amratian-
Gerzean) Period
about 3700–3200 B.C.

6

Dynasty I, greatly enlarged versions of these palettes
were carved with commemorative reliefs, including
ones depicting the deeds of rulers (see alcove D, case
D-1). Also characteristic of Gerzean art are the
painted pots in case B-7. These painted motifs often
portray scenes of river transportation, village shrines
and houses, and animals, as well as stick figures of
people in various attitudes; they should be compared
with the similar Gerzean painting in alcove A. Typical of art in this period are the small objects in case
B-5, while jewelry, ivories, and ceremonial maceheads are seen in case B-6. Of superb technical skill
and craftsmanship are the fine flint sickles, hoes,

11   Oracular statue of the god Horus as a falcon; serpentine, metalwork reconstructed.
10504
New Kingdom
about 1570–1070 B.C.

12 Isis, with Horus on
    her lap; bronze.
    10682
    Late Period
    Dynasty XXVI
    664–525 B.C.

axes, knives, and scrapers in case B-1. Flint knapping and stone carving were common and became fine arts because metal was rare; the stone vessels in case B-2 are extraordinary. Cores have been found showing that vessels were hollowed out with circular drills. Finally, case B-3 contains some of the luxury items found in the Royal Tombs at Abydos, one of the two major cemeteries for the First Dynasty: ivory furniture inlays and ornaments, copper pins and tools made from imported copper ore, and bracelets of stone and shell.

Alcove C (right)

The Predynastic pottery styles found in Alcove A gradually evolve into the *Pottery Styles of Pharaonic Egypt*. A representative collection of the vessels in daily use from the Old Kingdom to the New Kingdom is displayed in cases C-6 (3rd Dynasty and Old Kingdom), C-4 (Old Kingdom and First Intermediate Period), C-3 (Middle Kingdom), C-2 (Second Intermediate Period and early New Kingdom), and C-1 (New Kingdom). Of special interest here are the traces of foreign influence seen in the Levantine "Yahudiyeh" juglet of the Hyksos period (C-2 bot-

13 "The cat and the mouse bring in the little boy." Ostracon with a scene from a popular fable, or a caricature of a courtroom drama; painted limestone, inscribed on the reverse in hieratic.

13951
New Kingdom
Ramesside Period
Reigns of Sety I–Ramesses IV
about 1291–1145 B.C.

West Thebes
Deir el-Medina or
the Valley of the Kings

tom left), and the imports and influences from Cyprus and Syria-Palestine in C-2 (top two shelves) and C-1 (bottom shelf). These can be compared with the pottery in the Palestinian gallery. Stone vessels of the Old Kingdom had also reached a peak in craftsmanship and in case C-5 is displayed some of this work in alabaster.

Also of great interest are the indications of architecture provided by models (C-8) and excavations (C-7). The latter is a reconstruction of a house from Tell el-Amarna at the time of Akhenaton's (Dynasty XVIII) reign. It contains the estate's temple, stables, granaries, kitchen quarter, pool, and garden: all in all, quite a comfortable residence.

D Alcove D (left)

From the late Predynastic period onward, the most important source of knowledge of the Egyptians is their writing. The *Development of Egyptian Writing* over three thousand years, therefore, is of great concern to the Egyptologists who must decipher these written remains. The key to this decipherment was provided by the Rosetta Stone, a copy of which is seen in case D-8. The inscription on the stone is written in Greek and two varieties of Egyptian. But the earliest sort of writing derives from pictorial art: in the cast of the Narmer palette (case D-1), which apparently depicts the unification of the Nile valley around 3000 B.C., the name of Narmer is represented by a fish and a chisel. In the course of time, three kinds of script evolved in ancient Egypt. The first was hieroglyphic writing. The second was a more cursive style of writing, hieratic, out of which emerged around 700 B.C. a very rapid script, demotic. Samples of all these appear in cases D-3 to D-7, and they are particularly well represented in D-9. The cases include the various media used for writing: pots, statues, stelas, reliefs, and papyrus rolls. Shown in case D-2 are the various scribal tools used in writing: a palette with two colors of ink (red and black), a pen case, and a water jar, which were slung on the scribe's back.

14 Amun enthroned; bronze with gold foil armbands.
10584
Late Period
Dynasty XXVI
Reign of Amasis II
570–526 B.C.

15 Seated cat with incised
necklace, identified with
the goddess Bastet; bronze.
11390
Late Period
Dynasty XXVI–Ptolemaic
about 664–30 B.C.

E

20

Alcove E (right)

The Egyptians were not unlike us in their apprecia-
tion of the *Finer Things in Life*. This category includes
the personal ornamentation and toilet articles used in
daily life. Cases E-1 and E-3 include a variety of
necklaces with finely made beads. Drilled with a bow
drill, some bead holes are so narrow that modern
needles are too large to pass through. Other items
used in connection with cosmetics are displayed in
case E-2. Apart from the cosmetic containers, special
attention should be paid to the fine collection of
metal mirrors. Examples of Egyptian furniture
suggest a rather low and cramped posture for Egyptians at rest. In case E-5 is an alabaster table, while
chairs are seen in case E-7. Chairs were not common,
and served mainly to convey an air of superiority for
the user. Most upper-class Egyptians sat on stuffed

mats. Beds in earlier times were supported by legs in the shape of bulls' legs. The bed displayed here (case E-8) is probably of XVIII Dynasty date and has a neckrest which was used instead of pillows for the head. Home entertainment in this setting often comprised games using dice and knucklebones (case E-6 bottom shelf), and the playing of music (top shelf). The instruments exhibited here are early pipes, a New Kingdom harp, and two late sistra (ca. 550 B.C.) used by women in temples.

F   **Alcove F (left)**
The more mundane *Articles in Daily Use* include a remarkable display of preserved foods and kitchen utensils found in tombs; eggs, fowl, and coarse bread provided a not unappetizing menu (case F-1). Relat-

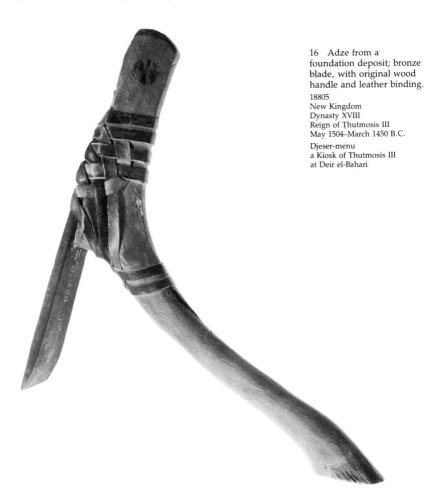

16   Adze from a foundation deposit; bronze blade, with original wood handle and leather binding.

18805
New Kingdom
Dynasty XVIII
Reign of Thutmosis III
May 1504–March 1450 B.C.

Djeser-menu
a Kiosk of Thutmosis III
at Deir el-Bahari

16

ing to construction work are the stamped mud bricks used for building (case F-2), the complete set of real and model tools used for farming and construction activities (case F-3), and a particularly good collection of similar tools (case F-7) from a foundation deposit within a building of Thutmosis III (Dynasty XVIII, New Kingdom). By this time, a standard range of high quality bronze tools was in production and use throughout the Near East. Case F-8 has well-preserved examples of basketry, linen, and other textiles, as well as the shuttles and loom pulleys used in weaving. Other articles of daily use include the pottery oven in case F-9 and the sealed storage jar in case F-4. A less common implement is the astronomical instrument used for stellar observations in case F-6, an indication of the rather sophisticated scientific expertise of the New Kingdom period.

17   Horus as a falcon, wearing the double crown of Upper and Lower Egypt; bronze.
17582
Late Period
Dynasty XXVI–Ptolemaic
about 664–30 B.C.

18 Head of an owl, a
sculptor's study or votive
plaque; limestone.
17972
Late Period
Dynasty XXVI–Ptolemaic
about 664–30 B.C.

19   Game of *senet* with its playing pieces; draughtboard of thirty
squares crafted atop a box with drawer for tokens; acacia wood and
Egyptian faience.
371   Akhmim
New Kingdom
Dynasties XVIII–XIX
about 1570–1185 B.C.

20   Re-strung jewelry
components from various
sources; Egyptian faience.
New Kingdom
about 1570–1070 B.C.

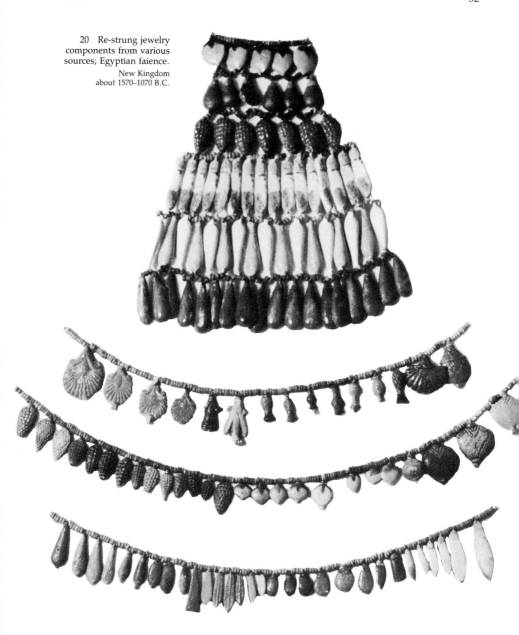

G

21

7
18
22

Alcove G (right)

Surely one of the most spectacular aspects of Egyptian cultural achievement is seen in their *Artistic Accomplishments*. The older traditional school of sculpture that first crystalized in the Old Kingdom period was quite formalized. In cases G-5, G-6, and G-7 the extension of these standards to human portraiture is seen in the idealized impersonal characteristics of the Egyptian lady and the god Ptah represented in formal pose. The humanizing art style of the Amarna period initiated under Akhenaton was an aberration (case G-4). It rendered its subject in more fluid movements with far freer lines and strokes. In human portraiture, facial features were distended and proportions were exaggerated The highly developed skills of the Egyptian artist can be seen in the sculptors' models in cases G-1 and G-3, where intricate detail in both human and animal figures was carved by the masters as guides for their pupils. The fine differentiation between figures can be seen in finished products in case G-2 where various foreigners are shown in great detail. To some extent, however, this was due to the highly stereotyped view of all foreigners that the Egyptians held.

H

11
12
14
15
17

Alcove H (left)

Egyptian Religion was not just a deeply motivating factor in the fears and aspirations of the king and common men, but a guide to the running of the state and society and to the understanding of the world. Connected to this religion are the use of personal amulets protraying the gods (cases H-1 and H-3), and the use of ritual vessels in ceremonies (H-2). Within the enormous pantheon, individual gods were represented both in anthropomorphic form and as specific animals (cases H-10, H-6, H-9, H-4).

Other characteristic features of Egyptian life were *Scarabs and Seals*, which were used to indicate ownership and as amulets. The earliest seals were either in stamp or cylinder form, the latter borrowed from Mesopotamia, but by the Middle Kingdom the scarab in the shape of a dung beetle was becoming popular. In cases H-7 and H-8, a wide assortment of early cylinder seals, stamp seals, ordinary and ceremonial scarabs, and signet rings is displayed. The scarabs in H-8 include ones inscribed with the names

21 Upper part of a life-
size statue of a god,
commissioned for a royal
jubilee; black granite.
10607
New Kingdom
Dynasty XVIII
last decade of the reign of
Amenhotep III
1359–1349 B.C.
probably from Thebes

and titles of officials and royalty. An important and
prominent aspect of Egyptian religion was the attitude toward the afterlife. One aspect of this is represented by the funerary monuments, of which the
"mastaba" was a common example. Some idea of
what the early "bench-like" mastabas looked like can
be gained from the model in case H-5, and the dis-
parity in scale with royal tombs can be observed by
comparing it with the pyramid complex of Sahure
(Dynasty V) at Abusir (in alcove J).

I | **Alcove I (right)**

The Theban dynasty that led Egypt in its quest for empire virtually ended with the death of the boy king Tutankhamun, when the power of the Eighteenth Dynasty was usurped by two high officials, Horemhab and Ai. The colossal statue of Tutankhamun that dominates this alcove was found in pieces on the west bank of Thebes, from where it was later shipped and restored. Of particular interest on this statue is the name of Horemhab that appears on the belt buckle; this usurper removed the name of Tutankhamun and replaced it with his own.

The remainder of this alcove and the following one portray the elaborate measures undertaken by the Egyptians to prepare for the afterlife. *Tomb Reliefs and Sculpture* were a major part of these measures. In both cases I-2 and I-3 (left of the doorway) are found a range of funerary stelas dating from the Old Kingdom to the Late Period. Notice that the art styles in

22 Striding figure of a ram, a sculptor's study or votive plaque; limestone.
18212 (formerly, Art Institute of Chicago 20.251)
Ptolemaic Period
332–30 B.C.

the early periods, Dynasties IV to VI, were formal and regimented, but by the First Intermediate Period the erection of major tombs in the provinces saw an explosion of experimentation with form and color, resulting in less refined, even gaudy depictions. By the Late Period, however, emulation of the past led to the copying of earlier styles. Case I-2 also includes statues and busts of the owner to provide a resting place for the soul should the mummy of the owner come to any harm.In case I-3 a "cluster column" from the enclosure wall of Medinet Habu (the mortuary temple of Ramesses III of the Twentieth Dynasty) displays some of the bright colors characteristic of Egyptian decoration.

23   Model of a
slaughterhouse/brewery/
bakery; wood, covered with
gesso and painted.
11495
First Intermediate Period
Dynasty IX
about 2200 B.C.
Sedment el-Gebel, Tomb 2105

Alcove J (left)   J

Considered vital to the successful afterlife of the king, the royal funerary complexes of the Old Kingdom were spectacularly massive. The model of the funerary pyramid complex of Sahure (ca. 2550 B.C.) at Abusir shows the intricate passageways, interior

rooms, and exterior service buildings and temples that formed the entire mortuary practice (case J-6).

Within the tombs, a variety of objects served specific purposes in the afterlife. In case J-1 is the largest known group of tomb statuettes; they were found at Giza (Dynasty V or VI). These depict household duties, while the wooden models (cases J-4 and J-5) display many kinds of activities that the owner hoped to enjoy in the afterlife. These cases show boats in the river and domestic scenes on the shore. In the foreground (right) are other activities pursued on the estate: cooking, beer making, and slaughtering. At the back is a model bakery. Model boats were an important part of the assembly, probably because they represented a river journey of pilgrimage to Abydos, a major center of the funerary cult. Paintings of activities on tomb walls in the Old Kingdom existed side by side with the figures of wood. In the Middle Kingdom, "ushabti's" appeared, proxy workmen intended to work in place of the deceased in the afterlife (case J-2).

During the first millennium B.C., painted wooden

23
24

24   Model of a Nile boat with its sail set for traveling upstream (southward); wood, covered with gesso and painted.
11492
First Intermediate Period
Dynasty IX
about 2200 B.C.
Sedment el-Gebel, Tomb 2105

plaques representing funerary rites and wooden statues depicting the gods were placed in the tomb and on the temple walls (case J-7).

The central feature of the tomb, of course, was the mummified body with the mummy mask, the coffin, and the extracted internal organs. Before preserving the body, the liver, intestines, lungs, and stomach were removed and placed in canopic jars (case J-3), so that each body had four jars accompanying it. The heart was left in the body. During the process of mummification by which the body itself was preserved, the body was heavily bandaged (cases J-12, J-13, J-14). To help preserve the identity of the deceased, masks were made to fit over the head of each mummy (J-14). Made of linen covered with stucco, painted and gilded, these masks were shaped and decorated to resemble the deceased during life. Case J-10 contains masks of women of the Later Period; the central one is decidedly foreign in appearance. The coffins in which the body was laid underwent considerable changes. The sarcophagus of the Old Kingdom had only the name and title of the deceased carved on it, while "pyramid texts" and other religious texts were placed on the walls of the pyramids of late V and VI Dynasty royalty. From the First Intermediate Period on, however, coffins were made of wood, and the texts were inscribed onto the coffin itself—"Coffin Texts" (case J-8). By the Late Period, coffins were no longer rectangular in shape but were made in anthropoid form (cases J-14, J-15).

Gallery End Displays
west end
Over the entrance is a reproduction of a relief depicting the victorious charge of Seti I (Dynasty XIX, ca. 1300 B.C.) against the nomads of Palestine. This motif of the conquering king in a chariot became common in the New Kingdom.

east end
At the end of the Egyptian gallery is the colossal winged bull-man-god found at the palace of the Assyrian king, Sargon II (721–705 B.C.), at Khorsabad in Iraq. This was one of several guarding the entrance to the throne room of the palace.

25

25 Human-headed winged bull; limestone.
A 7369
Neo-Assyrian Period
Reign of Sargon II
721–705 B.C.
Khorsabad
Palace of Sargon II

Assyria

ANCIENT ASSYRIA extended across the plains and foothills of what is generally called northern or upper Mesopotamia, the vast region between the Tigris and the Euphrates north of Baghdad in Iraq. The heartland of Assyria, however, lay in a rather small capital district on the banks of the Tigris. Nearly all the known Assyrian capitals lay on a relatively short stretch of river bank near where the tributaries of the Greater and Lesser Zab merged with the great river.

The name Assyria itself comes from the name of one of its longstanding capitals, Assur, which was also the name of the principal deity of the city. The region of Assyria was settled at an early stage of Mesopotamian history. Nineveh, one of the later Assyrian capitals, was occupied before 5000 B.C., while Assur itself was an important city by around 2500 B.C. The city of Assur came under the sway of the Akkadian and Ur III empires in the south (ca. 2334–2154 B.C. and 2112–2004 B.C.), but by about 1900 B.C., a small state had re-emerged and had begun to play an increasingly important role in Mesopotamian history. During the Old Assyrian period (ca. 2000 to 1760 B.C.), while Assur was ruled by an independent dynasty, the Assyrians established trading colonies in central Anatolia that were engaged in wide-ranging trade in textiles, tin, and silver. By around 1800 B.C., under Shamshi-Adad I and his sons, the Assyrians were able to establish political hegemony over most of northern Mesopotamia. The district capitals of this powerful state were the major cities of Ekallatum, Shubat-Enlil, and Mari, the last being a formerly independent city-state that was captured by Shamshi-Adad. The archives recovered from the excavations at this site attest to the foreign relations of the Assyrians with their neighbors to the south and west. This brief but brightly illuminated period draws to an abrupt close with the rise of Babylon under Hammurabi.

For the next four centuries, the Assyrian territories remained in the shadow of successive foreign powers, the Old Babylonian kingdom, the kingdom of

HISTORICAL VIEW

Khana, and the Mitannian regime. Around 1500 B.C., the Hurrian kingdom of Mitanni stretched across northern Mesopotamia and Syria, centered around the still enigmatic capital at Wasshukanni. Internal dissension and pressure from both the Hittites of Anatolia and the Assyrians, however, led to the rapid dissolution of the power and influence of the Mitannians around 1370 B.C. Into this vacuum stepped a renascent Assyria which, under Assur-uballit I (ca. 1363–1328 B.C.), ushered in the Middle Assyrian period (ca. 1363 to 935 B.C.). For another four centuries, Assyrian influence waxed and waned for brief moments under successive strong and weak kings. Under aggressive rulers like Adad-nirari I (1305–1274), Shalmaneser I (1273–1244), Tukulti-Ninurta I (1243–1207), and Tiglath-pileser I (1114–1076), Assyria slowly expanded as a world power, while at other times it could barely maintain its sovereignty.

After a century of relative weakness, the last and most explosive burst of Assyrian power and culture came in the Neo-Assyrian period (934–612 B.C.). This gradual rise from comparative obscurity in the 10th century reached its peak in the 8th and 7th centuries. A number of highly capable rulers expanded the borders into hitherto Babylonian, Syrian, Israelite, and Egyptian territories and laid the foundations of the mightiest empire the world had yet known. Centered at various times in the capitals of Assur, Nineveh, Calah (Nimrud), and Dur-Sharrukin (Khorsabad), the Assyrian empire relied upon a formidable war machine to maintain its hold over subjugated peoples and to sustain the tremendous cultural achievements—particularly building programs and artistic works—sponsored by the state. Perhaps the most enduring of those works were the large stone carved reliefs that lined the walls of the various palaces. To complete these projects, drastic measures—including mass deportations of provincial populations—were undertaken. For instance, over 27,000 citizens of the northern Israelite kingdom were sent to distant places. But, foreshadowed by revolts, the end came suddenly. After the fall of the capital, Nineveh, to a coalition of Babylonians and Medes in 612 B.C., Assyria was never again to rise as a major political force.

Anatolia

ANATOLIA, the Asiatic portion of modern Turkey, is broken up by long and high mountain ranges into a rugged terrain of alternating plateaus, valleys, and highlands. Historically divided into a number of diverse but interconnected cultural regions, Anatolia was always a formidable northern border for the ancient Near East.

Very little research has been undertaken into the earliest prehistoric periods of Anatolia, but early farming villages are now known from a number of important sites (Suberde, Çatal Hüyük, and Çayönü) in central southwestern Turkey, the Konya plain, and southeastern Turkey on the foothills of the Taurus mountains. The latter two sites reveal that a great deal of cultural sophistication, particularly in architecture, had already been attained between 7000 and 5500 B.C. In this early period, Anatolia was already the source of the distribution of obsidian throughout the Near East.

By around 3000 B.C., a number of regional cultures had developed to the stage of towns and kingdoms. Representative of these regional developments are the sites of Troy on the northwest coast, Alishar and Alaça Hüyük in central Anatolia, and a widespread culture in eastern Anatolia (called the "Early Transcaucasian Culture") represented by a glossy red and black burnished pottery. The appearance of kingship in this formative era is strongly suggested by the discovery at Alaça Hüyük of thirteen stone-lined shallow tombs containing numerous precious metal objects of superb handiwork. The earliest historical records from Anatolia, however, date to around 1900 B.C. A colony of Assyrian merchants was established in the independent city of Kanesh (modern Kültepe in central Anatolia) to pursue a lucrative long-distance business between Assyria and Kanesh. One of at least eleven such colonies in Anatolia, the community at Kanesh left records of extensive commerce in silver, tin, and textiles. Among the archaeological remains were cylinder seal impressions—with motifs influenced by Syrian, Anatolian, Babylonian, and

HISTORICAL VIEW

Assyrian styles—that illustrate the diverse connections maintained by the central Anatolians.

The independent cities of the central Anatolian plateau seem to have been incorporated into the expanding Hittite kingdom by about 1650 B.C. The Hittites, whose origins are obscure, spoke an Indo-European language that was written in a cuneiform script. Having settled on the central plateau possibly a few centuries earlier, they seem to be related to a certain king Anitta of Kusshara who lived at the time of the Assyrian colonies. In any case, records from the Hittite capital at Hattusha (modern Boghazköy)—the excavation of which provides our main source of knowledge about the Hittites—indicate that Anitta conquered both Kanesh and Hattusha, and that the founder of the Hittite dynastic line came from Kusshara.

Under two vigorous kings, the Hittite Old Kingdom (ca. 1650–1500 B.C.) rapidly expanded as far as north Syria, while military forays were carried out as far as Babylon. But amid internal chaos, this brief burst of Hittite power subsided into a period of obscurity. Roughly a century later, a new Hittite florescence ensued under the leadership of perhaps the greatest Hittite king, Suppiluliuma I. At the peak of its expansion, the Hittite New Kingdom or Empire period (ca. 1400–1200 B.C.) encompassed a large portion of the ancient Near East, extending over almost all of Anatolia and most of Syria where the Mitannians had been ousted, and competing with the Egyptians for Lebanon. Due to the many cultural influences that permeated Hittite society, Hittite documents were recorded in a number of languages, while Hittite religion included a vast number of deities drawn from other areas and peoples, particularly the Hurrians. Rock-cut reliefs were a characteristic feature of Hittite art, but even at Yazilikaya (where they are best represented), a shrine near Hattusha, the portrayal of the Hittite pantheon was accompanied by inscriptions indicating the Hurrian names of the principal gods.

The Hittite empire came to a rather abrupt end during the upheavals that wrenched the Near East around 1200 B.C. Following a period of relative obscurity, a number of regional groups emerged in Anatolia. In southeastern Turkey, a number of small city-states formed the southern territories of the former Hittite empire. The occupants of these new city-states, although probably more mixed than Hittite in origin, were called "Hittite" by their neighbors, used a Luwian or "Hieroglyphic Hittite" script, and worshipped Hittite/Hurrian gods. By the 9th century, however, some of these city-states were partly supplanted by Arameans, and by the 8th century the entire area had been virtually incorporated into the Neo-Assyrian empire.

In the 9th century, another important state, Urartu, arose in the highlands of eastern Turkey and northwestern Iran. Related to the earlier Hurrian population, the Urartians attained their peak about a century after their emergence as a unified kingdom, but, following a series of conflicts and conciliations with the Assyrians, Urartu fell shortly after 600 B.C.

In central Anatolia, a population of unknown origin called the Phrygians formed a kingdom by around the 8th century B.C. Known almost entirely from Greek sources, the kingdom of Phrygia is probably best remembered for its most notable king, the legendary Midas. Recent excavations, however, have shed light on the material culture of this obscure kingdom. It came to an end around the 7th century, after severe testing by invasions of Cimmerians.

The Phrygian kingdom was in part replaced by another population group, the Lydians. For a brief period between the fall of Phrygia and the rise of the Persians (in the east), the kingdom of Lydia expanded into the vacuum left by other powers, and from the capital at Sardis ruled a territory that extended from the western (Ionian) coast of Turkey to the mountains of eastern Anatolia. Like the Phrygians, the Lydians are known mainly from Greek sources, although excavations at Sardis and other sites have recently revealed information on their material culture. The kingdom ultimately succumbed to the mighty Persian empire. With the fall of this kingdom, Anatolia was not to have indigenous rule again until the Byzantine emperors established the capital of the eastern Roman empire in Constantinople. After Constantinople fell in 1453 A.D., the Ottoman Turks once again re-established Anatolia as a major Near Eastern power.

Syria

HISTORICAL VIEW

Most of what is now Syria, Jordan, Lebanon, and Israel was at one time referred to as Syria by the Greeks. In other times, the usage of this name became restricted to the northern half of the territory, including the coastal strip (Phoenicia) and the inland plateau west of the Euphrates (Coele Syria). Although the archaeology of Syria (in the restricted sense) is still very poorly known, some of the most important cave sites and villages to be excavated in the Near East are located in Syria. There are Paleolithic (before ca. 15,000 B.C.) cave sites in the Syro-Lebanese mountain ranges and Neolithic (ca. 8000–5000 B.C.) villages on the coast and interior.

Following the establishment of the first farming villages, there seems to have been continuous contact with Mesopotamia for most of the prehistoric periods, indicated primarily by the presence of Mesopotamian painted pottery styles in the Halaf and Ubaid traditions. By around 3500 B.C. there may have been a substantial presence of Mesopotamian settlers in northern Syria. A number of temple and town sites of clearly Mesopotamian origin have now been excavated as far north as southeastern Turkey. The first local cities apparently arose slightly later, about 3000 B.C., on the coast. At Byblos, for instance, a number of impressive temples with important Egyptian features were erected within a town wall. No later than about 2500 B.C., even more impressive cities like Ebla were formed in inland regions. The royal archives and art works found at Ebla, which was inhabited by a Semitic-speaking people, indicate that Syria, although strongly influenced by Mesopotamia, was by no means an insignificant backwater but was also a center of cultural, economic, and political development.

Other important kingdoms appear in historical records after about 2000 B.C. The most notable of these was the kingdom of Yamhad which, centered at the city of Aleppo, rivalled such major Mesopotamian kingdoms as Babylon and Assur in power and prestige. But other kingdoms to the west and south are also known, including Ebla, Qatna, and Byblos. At the latter site, excavations have uncovered a number of royal tombs with direct connections to the Egyptian Middle Kingdom pharaohs. After the Hittite capture of Babylon around 1600 B.C., Syria enters a dark age. When it emerges again into history, its many city-states are vassals or dependents of powerful foreign countries. Mitannians, Hittites, Egyptians, and Assyrians all competed for the control of Syria (at different times) with varying success. Under the Hittite sphere of influence was the kingdom of Ugarit, on the northern coast. At the heart of a wide-ranging network of international trade, Ugarit was also a center of the "Canaanite" culture that developed an alphabetic script. In Ugaritic, a language closely related to Hebrew, are preserved several literary documents of great interest for the pre-Biblical religion of the area.

The city-states of the Syrian Bronze Age and the foreign empires that dominated them dissolved around 1200 B.C. Over several obscure centuries, they were replaced by a number of ethnic groups occupying the same urban centers. The Phoenicians, direct descendants of the "Canaanites," occupied the coast and established colonies throughout the western Mediterranean. In the far north, a number of "Neo-Hittite" kingdoms that may have originated from the former dependencies of the Hittite empire formed a small ethnic minority. By far the most important group to appear at this time was the Arameans, who settled most of central and southern Syria and used an alphabetically-written Semitic language similar to Phoenician and Hebrew. At the peak of their development, the Arameans took over the "Neo-Hittite" kingdoms and came into conflict with the Israelites. This florescence was short-lived, however, for the rising power of Assyria soon resulted in the conquest and subjugation of Syria. After the 8th century, Syria came under the continuous domination of successive empires ruling from foreign capitals. Local rule did not occur again until 661 A.D., when the Umayyad Caliphate was established in Damascus.

GALLERY PLAN

Assyria, Anatolia and Syria

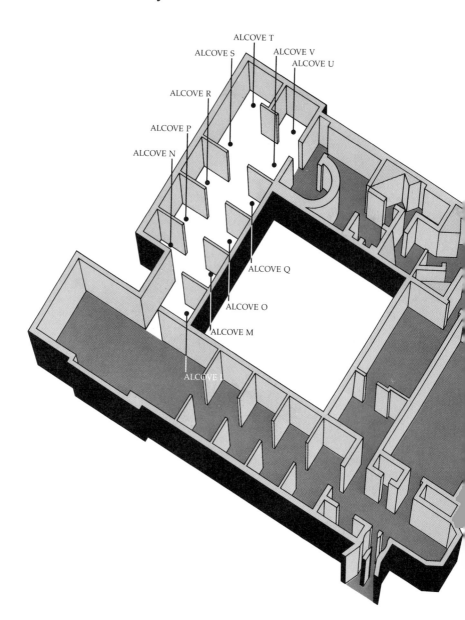

ALCOVE T
ALCOVE S
ALCOVE V
ALCOVE U
ALCOVE R
ALCOVE P
ALCOVE N
ALCOVE Q
ALCOVE O
ALCOVE M
ALCOVE L

The Assyrian, Anatolian, and Syrian gallery includes the Oriental Institute's collections from Assyria and a number of regions peripheral to the major civilizations of Egypt, Mesopotamia, and the Biblical world. Obtained largely from the Institute's excavations, the exhibits represent discoveries at specific sites rather than comprehensive coverage of the civilizations concerned.

Assyria
The Assyrian exhibits consist mainly of stone-cut wall reliefs of the Neo-Assyrian period (ca. 935–612 B.C.). Most were discovered in the course of the Oriental Institute's work at Dur-Sharrukin (Khorsabad) in Iraq, and date to the reign of Sargon II (721–705 B.C.). The reliefs belong to the palace of Sargon, where the principal rooms were lined with colossal relief sculpture. The winged bull in the Egyptian hall also comes from the gateway of this palace.

25

GALLERY EXHIBITS

Assyria, Anatolia and Syria

L

26

Alcove L (right)

The Assyrian reliefs here include ones depicting a groom with two horses, Sargon's conquest of Merodach-Baladan, and the head of an Assyrian official. There is also a fragment from the base of Sargon's throne.

At the back of this alcove is an exhibit of the finds from the Samarran site of Choga Mami. Located in the foothills of Iraq, Choga Mami dates to the sixth millennium B.C., when irrigation was first being practiced in southern Mesopotamia.

26 A Median groom walking two horses; limestone.
A 7358
Neo-Assyrian Period
Reign of Sargon II
721–705 B.C.
Khorsabad
Palace of Sargon II
Court VIII–10
Northwest Wall

M

Alcove M (right)

Another Assyrian capital with wall reliefs is Nimrud (Calah). The reliefs exhibited here are from the 9th century palace of Ashurnasirpal II (883–859 B.C.), and depict the head of the king and a winged protective being.

N

Alcove N (left)

There are two reliefs in this alcove, both originating from the palace of Sargon at Khorsabad. One depicts Sargon, king of Assyria, accompanied by an attendant. The other shows two Medes in procession, identified by their unusual clothing and boots.

27 Bull figure from the top of a standard; arsenical copper.
A 30798
Early Bronze Age
about 2300–2000 B.C.
Anatolia

O, Q

Alcoves O and Q (right)

These alcoves contain reliefs from the corridor connecting the official and residential sections of the palace at Khorsabad. Along this corridor were depicted figures of horses and men, captives from a foreign conquest; two typical examples are' shown here.

P, R

Alcoves P and R (left)

More reliefs from Khorsabad line the walls of these two alcoves. On both the left and right walls of alcove P and on the right wall of alcove R, the wall reliefs depict a procession of foreign captives and horses taken as booty on a military campaign.

T, U

35

28   Pair of stags or antelopes; painted pottery sherd from a large jar, wheel-made.
A 10266
Hittite Empire
Alishar IV Period
about 1400–1200 B.C.

Alcoves T (left) and U (right)

On the left walls of alcoves T and U are wall reliefs with similar motifs. These have three registers: a bottom register showing hunting scenes, a top register with scenes of a banquet, and a middle register

Alishar Hüyük

29 Bust of a human figure wearing a pigtail and a patterned garment from a very fine vessel decorated in high relief; pottery, polished reddish-yellow slip.
A 10958
Hittite Empire
about 1400–1200 B.C.

Alishar Hüyük

inscribed with the deeds and conquests of Sargon.

On the right walls of alcoves T and U and on the partition wall fronting the gallery entrance are three wall reliefs depicting court officials in various capacities. The relief in alcove T probably shows two military officials, while that along the partition wall shows eunuchs or attendants of the court. In alcove U, the right relief shows Sargon's prime minister and his attendant.

31

U | **Alcove U**

At the back of this alcove is a stone threshold found in the great hall of a residence adjoining the palace in the ciadel at Khorsabad. The carved decorations on this threshold may have imitated motifs on textiles. Next to the threshold is a stone altar, one of two found outside the gates of the citadel at Khorsabad. The altar is triangular in shape, and was probably dedicated by the king to an unknown deity. The bottom is carved to represent table legs, with the feet ending in lion's paws.

V | **Alcove V (right)**

Apart from wall reliefs, other examples of Assyrian accomplishments in architecture, writing, and crafts are displayed in this alcove. In the central display is a plan of the citadel at Khorsabad showing the major buildings and rooms excavated. Beneath this plan are various objects found in the rooms, including clay wall nails, bronze plaques with relief decoration, glazed bricks, and stone dishes. Drawings showing the original mounting of the Khorsabad winged bulls are also included.

On the left side of the Khorsabad display case are examples of Assyrian writing, including royal inscriptions and economic texts of the Middle and Neo-Assyrian periods (ca. 1363–935 and 934–612 B.C.). On the right side are examples of two distinctive kinds of painted pottery. The first is "Khabur Ware," a ceramic type found in Assyria and northern Mesopotamia during most of the Old Babylonian period and possibly earlier (ca. 1900–1600 B.C.). The second variety is so-called "Mitannian" or "Nuzi Ware," which is found in Assyria and northern Mesopotamia and Syria roughly during the period of the kingdom of Mitanni, and in substantial quantities at the site of Nuzi (ca. 1500–1200 B.C.).

30 Decorative plaque with a mythological scene in repoussé; bronze.
A 22209
Early Iron Age
Amuq, Phase 0
about 900–700 B.C.
Tell Tainat

31 Two Assyrian functionaries; limestone.
A 7366
Neo-Assyrian Period
Reign of Sargon II
721–705 B.C.
Khorsabad
Palace of Sargon II
Court VIII-25
Southwest Wall

32 Victorious Assyrian soldiers bear away the heads of slain Hittite
warriors, an example of Assyrian provincial art; limestone.
A 27854   Neo-Assyrian Period   about 750 B.C.   Tell Tainat

37   Also of interest in this alcove are bronze bands
decorated in relief encircling a wooden column,
found just outside the temple of Shamash (the Sun
God) in the citadel at Khorsabad. The bronze bands
shown here depict Sargon himself holding the horns
of two bulls. Flanking the entrance to this temple
were the two statues now placed beside the entrance
to the Mesopotamian hall. These stone statues depict
36   deities holding flasks of flowing water, a favorite
Mesopotamian motif.

Anatolia

The Oriental Institute's collection comes almost entirely from the excavations at Alishar Hüyük in central Anatolia. As such, it represents the material culture of only one Anatolian regional development, and lacks the more eclectic facets of Anatolian culture found in the western and southeastern regions.

Alcove N (left)

At the back of this alcove are two bulls made of copper, dating from the Anatolian Early Bronze Age. An unusual feature is the surface treatment—one half of each bull was covered with an arsenic-rich coating. While the copper surface has become corroded, the portion covered with the arsenic-rich metal remains essentially intact.

33 Decorated column base; basalt.
A 2785
8th century B.C.
Tell Tainat
royal palace of the
princes of Hattina

34 Goblet from the Amuq
Plain in the so-called
"Mitannian" style; light-on-
dark pottery.
A 27849
about 1270–1220 B.C.
Tell Tainat

P

Alcove P (left)

The most representative pottery of the Chalcolithic and Early Bronze Age (to ca. 2000 B.C.) from Alishar and Kültepe is displayed in the two cases in this alcove. Case P-3 contains Chalcolithic pottery sherds illustrating the variety of fine black ware, incised and impressed decorations, and painted pottery. Case P-4 contains mainly pottery from the Early Bronze Age, of which the red slipped and fluted varieties and the tall "fruit stands" deserve special attention. Also shown are the painted vessels of "Intermediate" ware from the later part of the Early Bronze Age. In case P-5 is a Cypriote figurine of a mother and child, dating to the 3rd millennium B.C.

R

Alcove R (left)

"Cappadocian" ware, a new painted pottery first appearing toward the end of the Early Bronze period, is exhibited in cases R-1 and R-4. Its use overlaps that of the pottery of the Middle Bronze (ca. 1900–1600 B.C.) period, when the Old Hittite kingdom was formed. Particularly characteristic of central Anatolian ceramics during this period is the red burnished and fine hard ware seen in case R-8. The high, sweeping spouts are also common in this period. Pottery of the Phrygian period is shown in cases R-3 and R-6, the latter with examples of the bichrome and gray ware of this time span.

Other objects from the Middle Bronze period and the Iron Age are to be found in cases R-2, R-4, and R-5. These include an infant burial jar, stamp seals

28

29

35 Hunting and banqueting scenes; limestone.

A 11255–56
Neo-Assyrian Period
Reign of Sargon II
721–705 B.C.
Khorsabad
Palace of Sargon II

and impressions, figurines, and medallions of the Middle Bronze Age. Also displayed are bronze pins and blades, bone work, and lead rings—possibly used as currency—of various periods.

Syria

The Syrian collection derives mainly from the excavations in the Amuq, in southeastern Turkey; however, a few objects from the Oriental Institute's work at other sites, including Tell Fakhariyah near the Khabur river, are included.

S

Alcove S (left)

On the left (Syrian) side of this alcove is exhibited some of the finer handiwork of Syrian craftsmen. The first case, S-2, displays metalwork from various periods. On the top and bottom shelves are small figurines, arrowheads, a mirror, and fibulae (early

30

safety pins). The triangular bronze plaque on the top shelf is an outstanding example of Iron Age metal artwork in north Syria, displaying both Near Eastern and Greek motifs. Of particular importance are the four figurines displayed on the middle shelf. These are made of tin bronze cast in a "lost-wax" method, and are among the earliest examples (ca. 3000 B.C.) of this alloy and this method of casting.

32

S-3 is a limestone relief orthostat found in Iron-Age Tayinat in the Amuq. Typical of north Syrian "Neo-Hittite" art in this period, it portrays a procession.

In case S-4 some fine examples of Iron Age stone-carving are displayed. In the middle row are steatite cosmetic jars, while the bottom row contains pouring bowls carved in the form of hands, with lion motifs, or with convoluted leaf patterns. On the top row is a limestone head of a deity found at Çatal Hüyük.

33

Between Alcoves S and T is a column base made of basalt from an Iron Age palace at Tell Tayinat.

T

Alcove T (left)

Pottery of different periods dominates the display in this alcove. The earliest Syrian pottery from the Amuq is shown in case T-3. On the bottom of the case are examples of local Neolithic pottery, pottery showing Mesopotamian influences from the Ubaid

36   Guardian deity holding a flowing vase; limestone.
A 11808
Neo-Assyrian Period
Reign of Sargon II
721–705 B.C.
Khorsabad
Temple of Nabu
Court, near the doorway

and Uruk cultures, and pottery of the Early Bronze "Khirbet Kerak" ware (also in case T-2). On the middle and top rows are specimens characteristic of the period ca. 2500–2000 B.C., the "Ebla Palace" period. Of particular interest here is an Anatolian two-handled cup (so-called "depas" goblet), a type well known from the excavations at Troy in northwestern Turkey.

The later periods are represented in case T-5, where pottery of the Late Bronze Age (ca. 1600–1200 B.C.) and the Iron Age (ca. 1200–700 B.C.) is displayed. On the top row are examples of "Mitannian" or "Nuzi" painted goblets, similar to those in the Assyrian display, but occasionally with Aegean motifs. The red jug is known as a "Syrian bottle." On the middle shelf are three small juglets imported from Cyprus and dating to the later Iron Age. Two are of the Black-on-Red tradition thought to be Phoenician in origin. Finally, on the bottom row are pottery vessels from the early Iron Age that show strong influences from Mycenean pottery. Also exhibited here is red burnished pottery from the later Iron Age that probably took its inspiration from the Phoenician pottery of this period.

Other examples of Syrian craftsmanship can be seen in the remaining exhibits. Case T-4 contains pottery and stone tripod bowls, while T-6 contains a small basalt sphinx from Iron Age Tell Tayinat. In case T-1 are two unique statues found in 2nd millennium B.C. deposits at Tell Fakhariyah in north Syria.

34

37 Detail of a scene showing the king mastering two bulls; bronze band from a wooden column.

A 12468   Khorsabad
Neo-Assyrian Period   Temple of Shamash
Reign of Sargon II
721–705 B.C.

Mesopotamia

"MESOPOTAMIA" is the land between the two rivers, the Euphrates and the Tigris. Both rivers have their sources in the high Taurus, near what is now Armenia. The Euphrates originates near Mount Ararat and then travels almost 1800 miles across the north Syrian steppe into the Arab-Iranian Gulf. The Tigris follows a shorter path of about 1150 miles along the edges of the Zagros Mountains. Near Baghdad the two rivers almost converge, but then they split until the last segment near Basra. The resulting topography is a broad upland plain stretching from northern Iraq to northern Syria, where the two rivers are widest apart, and a narrower silty depression south of Baghdad, where the Euphrates actually runs above the level of the plain. Traditionally, therefore, this extensive area has been divided into the south Mesopotamian lowlands, ancient Sumer and Babylonia, and the northern Mesopotamian uplands and foothills, ancient Assyria.

Bounded by rugged mountains to the east and north and by broad stretches of virtual desert to the west, Mesopotamian history has to some extent been influenced by the relationships of the people of the flood plains with their neighbors in the mountains or on the steppe. Then too, in a climatic zone where rainfall farming is practical only near the foothills of Assyria, the course of Mesopotamian history has been profoundly affected by the nature of the two rivercourses. The deeply-carved Tigris has been a useful source of water only since lifting devices became available. On the other hand, the Euphrates has been both a traffic artery and a source of life. But life on the southern alluvium has been both temperamental and precarious. Dependent entirely on the natural flooding of river water over the banks of levee deposits, survival has meant the diversion of water channels through the accumulating silt, the fallowing of fields tainted by waterborne salt, and the shifting of lifestyles when watercourses changed directions. Against this constant challenge, Mesopotamian civilization—a civilization essentially of cities—has

HISTORICAL VIEW

largely been a history of alternating success and failure: success in the periodic establishment of urban suzerainty over the countryside and over nomads, and failure in the inevitable loss of this overlordship to other towns and outsiders.

The beginnings of Mesopotamian civilization are to be sought in the highlands and upland plains. Small farming villages were initially founded on the foothills of the Zagros mountains (Jarmo), but shortly after 6000 B.C. more elaborate villages are to be found in the Assyrian uplands (Umm Dabaghiyah). From such poorly known beginnings there emerged before 5500 B.C. a number of separate cultures extending over most of northern and southern Mesopotamia. Farthest north, covering the broad Syrian steppe between the Euphrates and the Tigris, was the Halaf culture, which was characterized by a brilliant, at times multicolored, fine pottery and by buildings with keyhole plans (tholoi). Best represented at the site of Arpachiyah near modern Mosul, this culture flourished for about a thousand years, eventually spreading in an arc around the northern Fertile Crescent. Southwest of Mosul, a less spectacular culture has been excavated at Hassuna. Named after this site, the Hassuna culture was more restricted in area and lasted only until about 5000 B.C. Finally, around the middle Euphrates just north of Baghdad, there developed the Samarran culture. Noted for its architectural sophistication at the site of Tell es-Sawwan, and for a specific kind of painted pottery, the Samarran culture may also have been the first to develop irrigation agriculture. The villages belonging to this culture are entirely in areas with rainfall inadequate for dryfarming. These three cultures apparently coexisted for some time, with the Hassuna dying out first, the Samarran next, and the Halaf last, around 4500 B.C.

The Samarran gradually gave way to the Ubaid culture shortly after 5000 B.C., and this represents the earliest known occupation of the south Mesopotamian alluvium. Little is known of the early part of the Ubaid except for a series of small temples at the site of Eridu in the far south, a few small villages, and about 50 sites as far away as Saudi Arabia. But between 4500 and 4000 B.C. the pottery of this culture replaced the Halaf of the north and thus covered both northern and southern Mesopotamia. It is probably out of this tradition that there emerged around 3500 B.C., in the Uruk period, the first urban civilization in Mesopotamia and possibly the entire Near East. Remains at a number of ancient cities, but particularly at Uruk itself in the south, attest to the tremendous achievements of this period. Features of this first civilization include enormous temple complexes built on platforms and decorated with buttressed facades and "cone" mosaics, superbly carved cylinder seals (the first), and stone vases, and the appearance of the first writing—probably used for accounting—on small clay tablets. After brief influence as far away as Iran, Syria, and Turkey, and with but slight changes in material culture, the Uruk period phased into the Jemdet Nasr (ca. 3100–2900 B.C.) period, when writing, art, metallurgy, and presumably forms of government developed.

The Jemdet Nasr period is followed without a change in culture by the Early Dynastic period (ca. 2900–2334 B.C.), which is generally divided into three subperiods. Known mainly from the "Sumerian Kinglist" and some contemporary inscriptions and tablet archives, the age is one to which later tales of heroic exploits and legendary figures hark back. Certainly among the most famous of these tales are those of the Flood and of the great hero Gilgamesh of Uruk. It is thought that the first kings were established at this time, and certainly by Early Dynastic III (ca. 2600–2334 B.C.); the royal tombs at Ur give some hint as to the grandeur and wealth of the kingdoms. For divided into a number of constantly warring city-states, of which Kish, Uruk, Ur, Lagash, Umma, and Mari are perhaps the best known, the period is also a continuing narrative of changing supremacy under different cities, although all were religiously unified around the holy city of Nippur. The most detailed account of the period comes from the end of this heroic age, and depicts the long rivalry between Lagash and Umma. In the end, Umma finally won a short-lived victory. After a brief hegemony over Sumer, Lugalzaggesi of Umma and Uruk was defeated and his cities conquered by a usurper from Kish.

This conqueror, whose name was Sargon, ushered in a Semitic dynasty. With the full introduction of a Semitic language, Akkadian, Mesopotamia was never again to return completely to its earlier language, Sumerian. The Akkadian empire, named for its capital at Akkad in central Mesopotamia, unified all of Mesopotamia for the first time (ca. 2334–2154 B.C.). Thanks particularly to the efforts of Sargon and his grandson Naram-Sin, the military sway of the empire stretched to the Mediterranean to the west, Turkey to the north, and parts of Iran to the east, while its commercial enterprises involved long-range shipping through the Arab-Iranian Gulf. For the first time, Sargon could style himself "King of the Four Quarters of the World, King of Sumer and Akkad," while Naram-Sin could advance a step further to the status of a god. Near the end of the dynasty, ceaseless rebellions, constant wars on the frontiers, and palace revolutions finally took their toll, and for a brief moment Mesopotamia was at least partly ruled by foreigners called the Gutians (ca. 2154–2112 B.C.).

Following this chaotic interlude during which a number of city-states retained their autonomy, Utu-hegal of Uruk is credited with the final expulsion of the Gutians. A revival of Sumerian civilization, however, is often attributed to the rise of the Ur III dynasty (2112–2004 B.C.) under Ur-Nammu, a former governor of Ur, although a number of major artistic and literary achievements had been retained by Gudea of Lagash, probably during the Gutian interlude. Ur-Nammu's most notable achievements were the writing of a law code, the construction of several ziggurats (platform towers for religious purposes), and, not the least, the re-establishment of south-Mesopotamian hegemony over all of Mesopotamia. His successors were able to consolidate these holdings in a manner perhaps more cohesive than the Akkadian empire, to the extent that his son, Shulgi, was once again able to lay claim to the title of "King of the Four Quarters" as well as divine status. But, like its Akkadian predecessor, the Ur III empire ultimately collapsed, at least in part due to the rise of Semitic groups, the Amorites.

With the final disappearance of the Sumerians as a political force, the next four hundred years of Mesopotamian history are essentially the history of these new Amorite dynasties of the Isin-Larsa/Old Babylonian period (ca. 2004–1595 B.C.). The first to emerge was at the city of Isin, where a former general under the last Ur III king, Ishbi-Irra, was able to establish his rule. Isin was soon surpassed by its rival, the city of Larsa, and it in turn succumbed to the rising First Dynasty of Babylon. Under Hammurabi, Babylon was able to unite the south Mesopotamian plain and usher in the most brightly illuminated period of Mesopotamian history. Although faced by a number of powerful enemies at the beginning of his reign,

Hammurabi—perhaps best known for his law code—was able to expand his control as far as Assyria, Mari, Eshnunna, and Larsa. Under his successors, however, his achievements were rapidly eroded, in part by the encroachments of the Kassites and the First Sealand dynasty (in the far south). The final blow was struck by an invading Hittite force.

What followed for Babylonia was the longest period of rule under a single dynasty, the Kassites (1595–1155 B.C.). Emerging first around the middle Euphrates, the Kassite dynasty gradually took control of Babylonia and regained some of the territory lost by Hammurabi's successors. Later, a new capital was established at Dur-Kurigalzu (Aqar Quf) north of Babylon, and from there, a relatively stable reign was maintained until the Assyrian kingdom to the north began to grow in power. It was not the Assyrians, though, that finally overthrew the Kassites, but Elam to the east. With the end of the long-lived Kassite dynasty, Babylonia entered a long period of subordination. With the exception of the initial successors to the Kassites, the Second Dynasty of Isin, who were able to hold the Assyrians and Elamites for a brief time, until 626 B.C. Babylonia was ostensibly ruled by several (frequently ephemeral) local and foreign dynasties that were themselves under Assyrian control. A number of new population groups, including the Arameans and the Chaldeans, settled in the area, and near the end of Assyrian rule, the Babylonians contributed to the coalition that finally brought the Assyrian empire to an end.

The immediate heir to the Assyrian empire was the Neo-Babylonian empire (625–539 B.C.), which under a Chaldean dynasty was able to regain the lost possessions of the Assyrians. The most dynamic sovereign of this short-lived dynasty was Nebuchadnezzar II, whose reconstruction of Babylon and capture of Jerusalem may well have been the most notable achievements in an already illustrious career. A few decades later, Babylonia became part of the Persian empire (539–331 B.C.), and after Alexander's conquest, the Macedonian and Seleucid realm (331–126 B.C.). With Parthian (126 B.C. to 227 A.D.) rule, the cuneiform legacy of the Sumero-Akkadian civilization finally came to an end. The Sassanids (227–636 A.D.) followed before the Islamic invasion. Mesopotamia did not again become the center of a flourishing civilization until the Abbasid Caliphate (750–1258 A.D.).

GALLERY PLAN

Mesopotamia

The Mesopotamian collection of the Oriental Institute Museum is one of the largest and most representative in the United States. Mostly obtained from the Institute's excavations in Iraq, the objects displayed are, like the Egyptian collection, particularly effective for illustrating articles of daily life rather than monumental art and inscriptions.

39

38

Over the entrance to the Mesopotamian hall is a reconstruction of the Neo-Babylonian gateway which flanked the Processional Way in Babylon. This reconstruction incorporates original lion panels made of glazed bricks.

GALLERY EXHIBITS

Mesopotamia

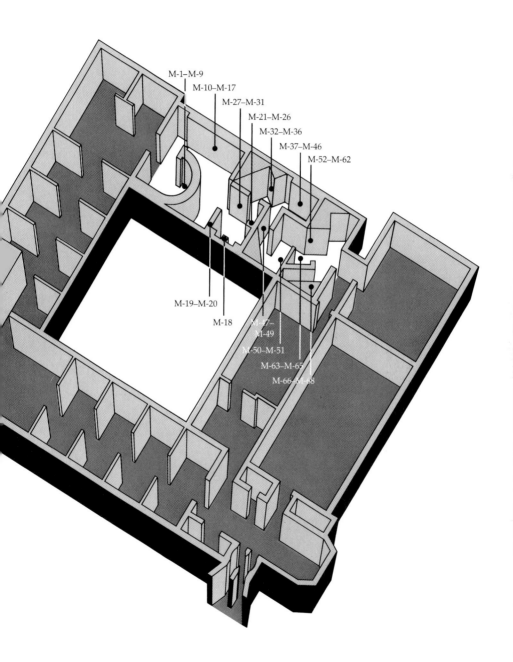

M-1–
M-9

38 Striding lion; glazed
brick, polychrome.
A 7481
Neo-Babylonian (Chaldean)
Period
Reign of Nebuchadnezzar II
604–562 B.C.
Babylon
from the processional
avenue before the
Ishtar Gate

Cases M-1 to M-9

A quick overview of the long *History and Cultural Development of Mesopotamia* begins with an introduction to the varied geography of the area. Composed of many ecological zones—mountains, foothills, plains, desert, marsh, and river banks—these different environments have been influential in the course of Mesopotamian history. In the following cases, objects—mostly pottery—typical of the successive historical periods, photographs of the major works of art, and a general account of important events and developments constitute each display. In the last five cases, dealing with the well-documented historical epochs, some of the more significant literature and sundry historical personalities are placed on the right-hand panel.

Cases M-1 and M-2 illustrate the early development of prehistoric cultures, from the domestication of plants and animals ca. 9000 B.C., to the first farming villages ca. 6000 B.C., to the subsequent formation of regional cultures in northern (Hassuna), cen-

39 The Ishtar Gate at Babylon in the time of Nebuchadnezzar II; oil painting by Maurice Bardin, after Professor Eckhard Unger, based on a watercolor by Herbert Anger.

40 The "Sennacherib
Prism," a record of his
eight military campaigns;
baked clay.
A 2793
Neo-Assyrian Period
Reign of Sennacherib
689 B.C.
Nineveh (Kuyunjik)

tral (Samarran), and southern Mesopotamia (early
Ubaid). The changeover to the Halaf culture in the
north and the gradual spread of Ubaid to all of Mesopotamia appear in M-2. With the Uruk-Jemdet Nasr
display in M-3, we enter the Protoliterate period
when writing first appears, as do the first cities,
magnificent temples, sculpture, mass-produced pottery, cylinder seals—all leading up to the first
stratified societies. By 2900 B.C., Mesopotamia was
divided into a number of city-states, ruled by local
kings of the Early Dynastic period. Written materials
now shed light on the heroes of this almost mythical
age, on the wars between the rulers of the city-states,
and on internal reforms and legislation within this
urban society (case M-4). In cases M-5 to M-9, the
later history of Mesopotamia unfolds, from the conquests of Sargon and the establishment of the Akkadian empire (M-5), through the collapse of this empire and the re-establishment of Neo-Sumerian
civilization under the Ur III kings (M-6), to the
breakup of this rule into disparate city-states that are
briefly unified under the brilliant reign of Hammurabi of Babylon (M-7); a copy of his famous law code
occupies the center of this area. The long and mostly
peaceful partition of Mesopotamia into Assyrian and
Babylonian states follows the fall of the Old Babylonian kingdom around 1600 B.C., and this endures
until the resurgence of Assyrian power shortly before
1000 B.C. (case M-8). Mesopotamia then enters its
last and most spectacular period of political power,
first under the Assyrian empire and then under the
Neo-Babylonian empire (M-9). By 539 B.C. this supremacy has given way to a Persian conquest.

Cases M-10 to M-17

10–
17

Possibly the most dramatic and certainly the most
visible remnants of the Mesopotamian past are the
architectural monuments of *Religious and Secular
Public Buildings*. The construction of temples was one
of the most important activities of a king's reign, and
each king left his mark in dedications in the form of
foundation deposits. Cases M-10 to M-16 illustrate
examples of these dedicatory offerings found in or
beneath temples: foundation deposits from one of
Gudea's temples in the Gutian or Ur III period
(M-10), a peg from the Early Dynastic period temple

oval at Khafaje (M-12), statuettes from the Ur III zig-gurat at Ur (M-13), tablets and clay nail inscriptions (M-14), and an inscribed cylinder commemorating the building of the ziggurat at Babylon in the Neo-Babylonian period (M-16). Characteristic bricks utilized in such temple constructions are displayed in case M-11, including bricks of the Protoliterate period, a "plano-convex" brick of the Early Dynastic I period, and bricks stamped with royal inscriptions from the Old Babylonian, Kassite, and Neo-Assyrian periods. Also an important feature of temple archi-tecture in the Protoliterate period are the "cone" or "nail" mosaics used to decorate walls and columns (case M-15). In the corner near case M-16 is a model of the Neo-Babylonian ziggurat at Babylon, possibly the inspiration for the Biblical "tower of Babel."

Secular public architecture is best represented by the royal palaces of Mesopotamia (M-17), the earliest of which is the Early Dynastic palace at Kish. Other palaces shown are the Old Babylonian palace at Mari and the palace of Sargon at Khorsabad (Dur-Sharrukin) in the Neo-Assyrian period. A record of military campaigns of Sennacherib in the Neo-As-syrian period written on a prism is also displayed, as is a gold tablet of Shalmaneser.

The greatest achievement of Mesopotamian civili-zation, however, lay not merely in its architecture but in its splendid cities. Above and next to M-17 are illustrations of some of the most significant cities: the relatively small city of Ur in the far south, the small provincial city of Eshnunna in central Mesopotamia, the holy city of Nippur, and the two great capitals of Nineveh and Babylon. The plans shown give some idea of the layout of public buildings within the cities.

40

M-18–
M-31

Cases M-18 to M-31

One of the highlights of Mesopotamian artistic achievement lay in the examples of *Sculpture* re-covered by archaeologists. The earliest examples of sculpture on a monumental scale are found in the Protoliterate period. Also typical are stone vessels carved in relief and miniature figures in the round (cases M-19 and M-20). The heart of the Oriental In-stitute's collections, however, is the Early Dynastic material found in the Diyala excavations. These in-

41 The provincial style in
Sumerian art, sculpture of
the third millennium B.C.
from the Diyala region;
stone.
A 12332
Tell Asmar
Square Temple of Abu
Shrine II
A 11441
Khafajah
Nintu Temple VII
A 18108
Tell Agrab
Shara Temple

41   clude the votive figures in M-21, M-23, and M-26, the
      votive plaques found on walls (M-25), and carved
      steatite and chlorite vessels, including the well-
      known vase from Bismaya depicting a procession of
      musicians carrying an unusual assortment of instru-
      ments (M-22). Both steatite and chlorite were mined
      in Iran and had to be transported to Mesopotamia
      across long distances. Sculptured stone cosmetic ves-
      sels are also seen in M-24. For the Akkadian through
      Neo-Assyrian periods, a series of small sculptured
      figures are shown in cases M-27 to M-31. These in-

42   clude a four-faced god and goddess of the Old Baby-
43   lonian period in M-27, the Bismaya Head—one of the
      finest pieces of Akkadian sculpture in the United
      States (M-28)—and a number of small pieces from the
      Old Babylonian, Isin-Larsa, Ur III, and Middle and
      Neo-Assyrian periods in M-29 to M-31.

32–   ## Cases M-32 to M-36
36   The most important single source for our knowledge
      of Mesopotamia comes from the numerous examples
      of *Writing*. This appears in the late fourth millennium
      B.C. for record-keeping purposes. The script, in
      "cuneiform," was first used for the Sumerian lan-
      guage, but later became adapted for various Semitic
      languages, most importantly Akkadian. Sumerian
      finally went out of use in the Old Babylonian period,
      and around the first millennium B.C., Aramaic, an
      alphabetically written Northwest Semitic language,
      was introduced and utilized alongside Akkadian.
      Cuneiform lasted until around 75 A.D. Case M-32
      illustrates this long usage of cuneiform and its appli-
      cation to these languages, particularly on clay tablets.
      Scribes were trained to write cuneiform, and M-33
      shows examples of school texts and copies, gram-
      matical texts, and syllabaries used in this training.
      Most documents record aspects of economic affairs
      (hundreds of thousands have been recovered), but
      there are many examples of legal texts, letters, in-
      scribed objects, and texts of a historical nature or
      royal record, and traditions in such scholarly subjects
      as medicine, literature, astronomy, and mathematics
      (cases M-34 to M-36).

42   Two four-faced deities; bronze.
A 7119
A 7120
First Dynasty of Babylon
1894–1595 B.C.   Ishchali

M-37–
M-46

Cases M-37 to M-46

Seals, particularly in the form of a cylinder, were one of the most characteristic features of Mesopotamian art. Utilized initially probably as a mark of ownership or as a trademark, the seal was probably also used for the safeguarding of possessions. The Oriental Institute's collection of seals, which is one of the world's finest, is represented here by about 200 items, and impressions of these "signatures" are displayed on modern rollings next to the seal itself. Also included in the exhibit are examples of ancient rollings on documents and jar "sealings" or covers. In the earliest period, "stamp" seals were used for making impressions on clay (M-37). By 3500 B.C., however, round cylinders were rolled across clay to make an impression of the design (M-38). Specific designs characterize each period. The early seals show schematic rows of animals or representations of other figures (M-38), and these are followed in the Jemdet Nasr period by geometric patterns (M-39). By Early Dynastic I, a "brocade" style comes into use, to be followed by a representational motif of combat between hero and animals in the later Early Dynastic period (M-40, M-41). This theme, presented in a more orderly fashion, continues into the Akkadian period (M-42), although it is accompanied by a greater variety of motifs (M-43). The presentation of individuals before a god is the most popular topic on seals of the 2nd millennium B.C., although by Kassite times, large inscriptions also appear on them (M-44). The Assyrian and Neo-Babylonian seals stress opposed groups of animals and men (M-45), and by the Persian and Seleucid times, stamp seals become popular again (M-46).

44

45

M-47–
M-51

Cases M-47 to M-51

Three major aspects of *Mesopotamian Religion* were the pantheon of gods, the temple cult, and personal or individual beliefs. The Mesopotamian pantheon encompassed many gods, and over the millennia, the character of these divine personalities and the world view that they represented changed. From the gods as providers to the gods as rulers of a world polity, and from the gods as divine forces to the gods as parents, what we know from literature of Mesopotamian divinities points to their important place as

43   The "Bismaya Head,"
from a male statuette;
white stone.
A 173
Dynasty of Akkad
2334–2154 B.C.
Bismaya (Adab)

metaphors for the human condition. Some idea of
who the major gods were, how they were related,
which cities they were most closely associated with,
how they were depicted, and how their characters
changed with time can be seen in case M-47. The
chronological chart shows how eight of the more important deities were perceived in different periods,
and a group of clay plaques demonstrates how they
were pictured by ordinary people.

Cases M-48 and M-49 form an exhibit illustrating
another important facet of religious life, the temple
organization and cult. The gods were cared for in

temple rituals that were probably affirmations of faith and devotion. Both ritual texts and ritual objects have been recovered from ancient ruins. Within the temples, the most sacred area was an inner room or sanctuary where a representation of the deity was displayed and accompanied by "cultic" objects and offerings used in ceremonies and rituals. The Mesopotamian temples—or at least the major ones—were large "public" institutions to which individuals probably had very little access. They were maintained by a professional priesthood.

The religious life of the private individual was

44 Running antelopes; cylinder seal impression.
A 30795
Early Dynastic I Period
about 2900–2750 B.C.

45 Mesopotamian seal-cutters attained a high level of achievement in the glyptic arts.
A 30802
First Dynasty of Babylon 1894–1595 B.C.
A 30794
Dynasty of Akkad 2334–2154 B.C.
A 30801
First Dynasty of Babylon 1894–1595 B.C.
A 30803
Neo-Assyrian Period about 750–650 B.C.

more probably one centered around spirits, demons, witches, ghosts, and other basic animistic and natural forces. In this world view of magic and personal gods, the practice of religion was probably largely concerned with the appeasement of such forces through incantations, spells, amulets, and personal devotions (M-50, M-51). In the exhibit, quotations from ancient texts and the means taken to combat and cope with the general conditions that commonly beset people are displayed. One important demon is Pazuzu, represented in case M-51.

46

M-52–
M-57

Cases M-52 to M-57

The *Crafts* of Mesopotamia were one of the main cultural achievements of the region. Although the

country lacked numerous mineral resources, craft specializations arose to meet the challenge of foreign and domestic demand. The making of pottery is illustrated in M-52 by photos of a kiln, a possible pottery wheel, and examples of pottery vessels and figurines. Because pottery is porous, watertight containers were made by coating the ceramic with a vitreous layer or glaze. This process came into use around 3000 B.C., but was more common after about 1400 B.C. Also in early use was glass, which appeared around 2400 B.C. but became more popular after 1600 B.C. (M-53).

Stoneworking began very early with the use of flint tools, but soon developed into an even more sophisticated art with the development of seal cutting, the making of stone vessels and beads, and the carving of sculpture. In case M-54, examples of these skills and how they were practiced are shown. Of particular interest are the specimens of fine stone bowls in various stages of manufacture, and cylinder seals with examples of tools used in their manufacture.

The most prominent crafts, however, were the manufacture of cloth and of reed and wood articles (M-55). Because of the basic lack of adequate timber, supplies of wood had to be obtained from distant places. Reeds were far more common and were utilized for matting, basketry, furniture, and even housing. Photographs of a modern reed shelter are shown in this display. The manufacture of textiles was a major part of the Mesopotamian economy; the raw materials were flax (for linen) and sheep's wool. Objects used in this craft are shown, along with a statue of a woman in a wool dress. The production of textiles figures prominently in written documents, and their export to foreign countries was sometimes practiced on a large scale.

Although metal was scarce, metallurgy and the use of metal for adornment and tools were important in Mesopotamia. Gold and silver were also used as a medium of exchange in place of a genuine currency, while copper and its alloy, bronze (i.e., with over 3% tin added to the copper), were extensively sought for use in vessels and implements. The heart of the display in cases M-56 and M-57 is a collection of copper vessels found in a level dating to around 2300 B.C. in the Oriental Institute's excavations at Eshnunna.

46 The demon Pazuzu; bronze.
A 25413
about 800–600 B.C.

M-58

Case M-58

Subsistence in Mesopotamia was centered around agriculture and animal husbandry. The alluvial soil of the Mesopotamian flood plain was irrigated by canals in order to grow cereal crops and dates. Vegetable gardens may have surrounded date groves and supplemented the daily diet. Beyond the cultivated fields, the herding of sheep and some goats and cattle was important for obtaining dairy products, wool, and hides. Around the rivers, fishing was also significant, but hunting probably became secondary after the prehistoric periods. Case M-58 emphasizes the physical remains of implements used in these activities: sickles and flints for harvesting and threshing grain, fishhooks and nets, projectiles for hunting and representations of animals hunted, herded animals, and implements used in spinning and weighing wool.

M-59–
M-62

Cases M-59 to M-62

trade, travel, economy, society, and war form the focus of this exhibit on *Foreign Contacts*. Numerous detailed documents and archaeological results give us a fairly vivid picture of the role and importance of trade between Mesopotamia and other regions. Lacking numerous natural resources, particularly stone, timber, and metals, the Mesopotamians imported these and other products, often in return for manufactured goods and transshipped products. Case M-59 provides an idea of the goods and routes involved in foreign trade. Transportation was in part provided by boats up the Euphrates or down the Arab-Iranian Gulf, but land travel by wheeled vehicles and beasts of burden was also used. Some of these vehicles and animals are displayed in Case M-60. The social and economic facets of Mesopotamian life were enormously complex. A simplified chart indicating the components of society appears in M-61. In this display, the relationships between the king and palace, the temple and priests, private individuals, foreign powers, army, and the city-state in general are indicated, as are the various social classes that formed Mesopotamian society. In the main, the government was in the hands of palace and city officials, while trade was carried out in both a private and public sector. Some representative objects of economic life are the calibrated stone weights used for measurement, the stone land sale document, and the silver coils used as a precursor of currency. War was a common phenomenon of Mesopotamian life, and case M-62 exhibits examples of weapons and illustrations of documents—epigraphic or representational—recording the occurrence of wars over boundaries, particularly the long-standing dispute between the cities of Lagash and Umma in the mid-third millennium.

Cases M-63 to M-68

3–
8

Our knowledge of *Daily Life* comes mainly from the excavation of numerous cities, although representations and written documents also provide much information on this subject. Thousands of private houses have been exposed by the archaeologist's spade, with remains of daily life still left in them. Prominent among these remains are those of dress and ornament. Cases M-63 to M-65 show cosmetic jars and utensils, bangles, necklaces, bracelets, anklets, medallions, bone and metal pins, and cylindrical beads which were used for personal ornamentation, as well as illustrations of how they were used. In case M-65, various styles of dress are depicted by representations and illustrations. Games are shown in case M-66, including board games and gaming pieces, representations of athletic events like wrestling, and what may be toy models and rattles. Music was also another form of entertainment, and in case M-68 representations of various instruments are displayed. Of interest in this regard are the texts recording musical notation, among which a cultic song from Ugarit is particularly significant. The setting for daily life in the city is the subject of case M-67. Here, a mockup of a typical private house and courtyard has been reconstructed with household pottery from around 1800 B.C. in its setting. To the right, the placing of such houses in towns can be seen from the plans of cities and photographs of excavated houses and streets. Also of interest in this regard are the burials sometimes associated with houses. Finally, the legal structure of family life, especially the laws for marriage, divorce, and inheritance, are noted in this display.

Iran

THE MODERN COUNTRY of Iran, the land of the Aryans and the country called Persia by the Greeks, is roughly three times the size of France. Most of this area is sharply defined by a ring of natural barriers: the Caspian Sea and Elburz Mountains to the north, the Arab-Iranian Gulf to the south, the Zagros Mountains to the west, and mountains and deserts to the east. The region is formed in the shape of a vast bowl, whose interior is a large expanse of mainly arid salt deserts. The principal means of access into Iran, therefore, has been by the lowlands of the northeast (from Central Asia) and the southwest (from Mesopotamia). But although the main communications both into and out of Iran have been with Mesopotamia and Central Asia, contacts have always been maintained to some degree with neighboring Pakistan, Afghanistan, and Turkey.

On this geographically diverse landscape, the principal centers of population and cultural development have been concentrated in the more amenable terrain of the west and north, in the modern provinces of Azerbaijan, Luristan, Kurdistan, Khuzistan, and Fars, and in Gilan and Mazanderan. There, the population has resided in the upland plains, in the irrigated lowlands, or as nomads in both zones. This does not mean that the eastern portions of Iran were unsettled, however. As a source of valuable minerals—particularly such precious stones as turquoise and steatite—and as a thoroughfare to the east, the central and eastern regions of Iran have been traversed by a number of important trade routes. Along these routes, important trade centers and way stations were founded in antiquity.

Perhaps because of the intensive archaeological research in western Iran, the earliest village settlements are to be found in the Zagros mountains and nearby, although even earlier cave sites have been excavated on the Caspian shoreline. Between 8500 B.C. and 7000 B.C., both plano-convex bricks and solid mud walls were used in constructing clusters of substantial rectangular rooms and small cubicles at Ganj

HISTORICAL
VIEW

Dareh in southern Kurdistan. With this fairly sophisticated architecture a very crude pottery was found, the earliest in the Middle East. At this point plants were still not domesticated, although goats may have been reared. However, by 6000 B.C. food producing villages are known at Tepe Guran in Azerbaijan and at Ali Kosh in Khuzistan. And by 5000 B.C. early farming villages, some producing a finely-decorated pottery repertoire, are known from several different regions. Two such regions are Fars and Khuzistan, where the respective sites of Bakun and Chogha Mish provide a striking collection of painted ceramics bearing both geometric motifs and representations of human and animal figures. By about 4000 B.C. the long tradition of fine painted pottery at Chogha Mish, known as the Susiana sequence in Khuzistan, after the site of Susa, is followed by the elegant Susa style.

Although interconnections between Khuzistan and the neighboring Mesopotamian floodplain existed prior to 3500 B.C., they became particularly prominent during the Protoliterate period (ca. 3500–3100 B.C.), when the first cities arose at Susa and Chogha Mish. The close cultural affinities between southern Mesopotamia and the Khuzistan region—geographically part of the same plain—were only the heart of a widespread web of commercial relations that extended into central and eastern Iran. For the first time, clay tablets inscribed in "Proto-Elamite"—a totally unintelligible script—or with numerical notations are found at a number of widely dispersed settlements: at Susa, Chogha Mish, and Tall-i-Ghazir in Khuzistan, at Godin Tepe in Luristan, at Tepe Sialk near Kashan, at Tepe Malyan in Fars, and at Tepe Yahya in Kerman. Mesopotamian-style Protoliterate cylinder seals replace stamp seals in this period, and are found at all these sites as either seal impressions on clay or the actual seals themselves. Also indicative of the long-distance trade that connected Mesopotamia via the Iranian plateau to Khorasan and Seistan are the carved chlorite vessels that were apparently produced at Yahya—and are found from Mesopotamia to the Indus Valley—and lapis lazuli, which may have come from Afghanistan through the frontier town of Shahr-i-Sokhta.

The history of Iran for the next two thousand or so

years (ca. 3000 to 1000 B.C.) is very much the history of Elam—southwestern Iran—as seen through Mesopotamian eyes. During the Mesopotamian Early Dynastic period, there are records of wars between Elam and Lagash, Kish, and Ur, and during the period of Akkadian imperial expansion shortly after, the cities of Susa and Awan—then under the first known Elamite dynasty—came briefly under Mesopotamian domination. The first important historical inscriptions written in Elamite come from this period, and they include a treaty with the Akkadians found at Susa. During the Ur III period in Mesopotamia, a new dynasty of Elamite rulers arose at Shimashki. This in turn was followed by a powerful new dynasty that lasted until at least about 1600 B.C., or concurrently with the Amorite dynasties of Isin, Larsa, and Babylon in southern Mesopotamia. The land of Elam was united at this time under a high king who took the title *sukkalmah* or "Grand Regent," with subsidiary positions held by a *sukkal* or "viceroy" of Elam and Shimashki, and a *sukkal* of Susa. For much of this period, Elam more than held its own against its Mesopotamian neighbors to the west, but with the decline of Babylon after Hammurabi, the history of Elam gradually fades into a list of poorly known kings. By around 1600 B.C., or roughly when the Kassites appear in Mesopotamia, the end of the Early Elamite Period becomes enshrouded in mystery. Although archaeological excavations have yielded substantial light on the material culture of Iran in the second millennium B.C. (e.g., Tepe Giyan, Tepe Hissar, Tureng Tepe, Hasanlu, Dinkha, Godin, and Yanik Tepe), by and large this evidence bears little relationship to the fragmentary historical evidence. Susa and the site of Haft Tepe are among the few excavations having archaeological remains that pertain directly to the early history of Elam.

About three centuries later, Elam re-emerges into history, entering the most brilliant phase of its civilization in the Middle Elamite Period. A new dynasty of rulers, first mentioned around 1300 B.C., styling themselves "King of Anshan and Susa" and "Expander of the Empire" led a resurgent Elam into a period of imperial conquests and major construction works. Undoubtedly aided by the disintegration of Kassite power in the west, the Elamites expanded into this political vacuum and began to encroach slowly into

Babylonian territory. After a sporadic series of raids under earlier monarchs, Elam finally emerged triumphant over what was left of Kassite Babylonia during the reign of Shutruk-Nahhunte (ca. 1185–1155 B.C.), Kutir-Nahhunte (1155–1150 B.C.), and Shilhak-Inshushinak (ca. 1150–1120 B.C.). The cities of Babylonia were attacked and taken, and major monuments including the statue of Marduk and the law code of Hammurabi were taken back to Elam as booty.

Archaeological investigations at Susa and Tepe Malyan (the ancient Anshan—one of the Elamite capital cities) have shed light on the Elamite civilization of this period, but the main architectural monument so far discovered is the citadel and ziggurat at Chogha Zanbil (Dur-Untash) in Khuzistan. Both tablets and inscriptions written in Elamite have been found.

Shortly after 1100 B.C., the history of the Elamites fades into obscurity for another 300 years. But at the same time as the disintegration of their power after the reign of Shilhak-Inshushinak, new kingdoms were forming farther to the north, and new population groups were entering Iran. Since historical records are vague on these new groups and kingdoms before about 900 B.C., archaeological remains provide the principal clues for unraveling the history of this period. A new type of pottery, a well-made gray ware, for instance, begins to replace the old painted styles of ceramics at a number of sites, and this has been interpreted to mean a movement of influences from the east to the west. In Luristan, numerous bronze artifacts—weaponry, personal ornaments, and "standards"—appear to be associated with a local culture which, according to the excavations at Baba Jan, would appear to have attained a degree of sophistication. A similar degree of sophistication, possibly reflecting a local aristocracy, may be indicated by the rich tombs at Marlik in northern Iran. At Hasanlu in Azerbaijan, excavations have revealed an important settlement of Manneans (of the kingdom of Manna) that was captured by the Urarteans. Apparently emerging in Azerbaijan and eastern Turkey at this time, the Urarteans also founded a citadel at Bastam. Similarly, citadels of the newly arrived Medes have been excavated at Godin and Nus-i-Jan in Luristan where the Medes settled and gradually formed an empire. The sort of picture that emerges then, for the period from 1100 to 600 B.C., is one in which a number of small kingdoms arose in the Zagros Mountains but were quickly absorbed by the Assyrians to the west, the Urarteans to the north, and the Medes to the south and east. When the Assyrians and Urarteans finally collapsed around 600 B.C., the Medes were able to expand briefly into the vacuum left by these major powers.

Among the Median vassals in Iran were the Persians, who had entered Iran at roughly the same time as the Medes, beginning around 1200 B.C. After a long period of subservience to the Medes, the Persians under the leadership of Cyrus—of the Achaemenid clan—were able to defeat the Medes in the Persian homeland of Fars in 550 B.C. In doing so, the Persians inherited the empire left by the Assyrians, Medes, and Babylonians—except that the achievements of the Persian empire exceeded those of all its predecessors. In quick succession, Babylonia, Anatolia, Palestine, and later Egypt were consolidated into the empire. At its height under Darius I (521–486 B.C.), the Persian empire extended from Libya and Turkey in the west to India in the east. This vast domain was administered in a manner quite unlike the Neo-Assyrian and Neo-Babylonian empires that preceded it in that provincial populations were to a great extent allowed a degree of autonomy including the preservation of local customs. Laws, religions, and languages therefore retained their regional and ethnic flavors. Yet the broad expanses of the empire were kept cohesive by an efficient system of imperial highways and courier services.

Much of the Achaemenid achievement tends to be associated with particularly notable kings and their capitals, and they present a view of the Persians that differs considerably from the information that we get from the Greeks, one of their principal opponents and our main historical source. Cyrus the Great (538–530 B.C.), who defeated the Medes and founded the empire, was viewed by the Babylonians as a savior for his reforms and restoration of the cult of Marduk. In Jerusalem, he magnanimously ordered the rebuilding of the temple. His new capital at Pasargadae—adorned with a new style of art that was uniquely Achaemenid—stands as an eloquent testimony to his reign. The Greek sources again portray

Cambyses (529–522 B.C.), Cyrus' son and successor, in a derogatory light but the Egyptian sources viewed him differently. Finally, Darius the Great, the author of the Behistun inscription—the Rosetta Stone of cuneiform—was responsible not only for cutting a canal from the Nile to the Red Sea, but also for the founding of a new capital at Persepolis in Fars province. Built by an international corps of craftsmen from the subject provinces, the monumental art and architecture of Persepolis represent a blending of both eastern and western elements into large and lofty halls with ornately carved columns, colossal guardian bulls and man-bulls, and long panels of stone reliefs.

The demise of the Achaemenid empire under the onslaught of the Macedonian king, Alexander the Great, is well known. After the battle of Arbela in 331 B.C., Iran became a Macedonian province which on the death of Alexander was ceded to Seleucus. The Seleucid era in Iran came to an end when the Parthians wrested control of the country from them in the second century A.D. Parthian rule in turn was lost to the Sassanians, who came to power in 224 A.D. Islamic rule came to Iran in the seventh century A.D., as to most of the Near East.

GALLERY PLAN

Iran

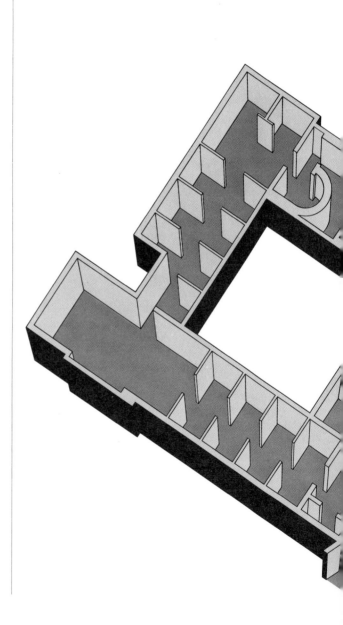

GALLERY EXHIBITS

Iran

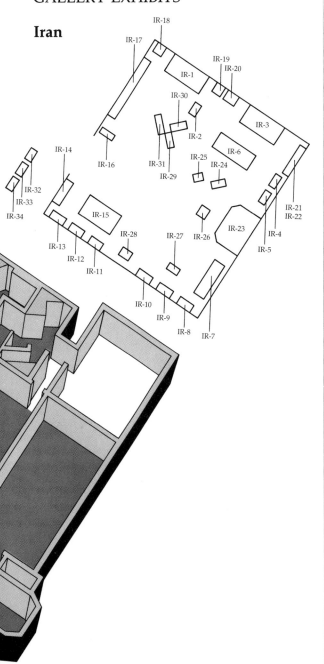

47   Head of a colossal bull; dark gray limestone.

A 24065   Achaemenid Period   Reigns of Xerxes I/Artaxerxes I   486–424 B.C.
Persepolis   Hundred-Column Hall from the anta on the east side of the portico

A major portion of the Oriental Institute's collection from Iran comes from its own excavations at Persepolis, Tall-i-Bakun, and Chogha Mish. Also included are purchased bronzes from Luristan and items from the collections of Ernst Herzfeld, the excavator of Persepolis, and other foreign excavations. The exhibits are not laid out in strict chronological order, but all the earliest material is displayed on the left side of the hall while all the material on the right side is ca. 1250 B.C. or later (Iron Age).

The exhibit descriptions below proceed clockwise around the hall beginning to the left of the entrance on the south wall, according to the chronological and cultural groupings.

-1–
-3

Prehistoric Pottery

Case IR-1 contains pottery from Tepe Giyan in central western Iran. The group spans the 3rd millennium and the 2nd millennium down to about 1300 B.C. The 3rd millennium pottery is from Giyan level III and is characterized by jars with sharp shoulders and stylized and geometric spread-eagle motifs, possibly derived from Susa in an earlier period. By level II at Tepe Giyan, bag-shaped pots had developed out of the sharp-shouldered shapes, and tripod bowls were also characteristic of the early 2nd millennium B.C. In the later 2nd millennium, Mesopotamian elements appear in Giyan level II, including the Mitannian-style goblets with concave sides and button-base vases of the Kassite period. Another regional development for the prehistoric periods, from the 6th–5th millennium B.C., is represented by the groups of vessels from Saveh in the central plateau (case IR-2). Pottery and small objects of the 4th millennium B.C. from Tall-i-Bakun near Persepolis are shown in case IR-3. The pottery is made of a fine buff ware and painted with geometric or naturalistic motifs, including ibexes with stylized horns. The small objects include stamp seals and figurines.

11
Another variation in the prehistoric periods is that from southeast of the Caspian Sea (case IR-11, on the right of the gallery, top row), at Tepe Hissar and Tureng Tepe. These vessels date to the 4th and early 3rd millennia B.C., and illustrate another style of painted pottery used in Iran prior to the introduction of Gray Burnished ware.

IR-4– IR-6

The Susiana Sequence from Chogha Mish

The prehistoric sequence in Khuzistan was first identified at the site of Susa by French archaeologists working at that site. Since then, this prehistoric sequence—named the Susiana sequence—has been modified by the excavations at Chogha Mish. Preceding the known Susiana sequence was the Archaic period (roughly 7000 B.C.), which was then followed by the earliest phase of the Susiana sequence, the Early Susiana period (ca. 6000 B.C.). From the Middle Susiana (ca. 5000 B.C.) to the Late Susiana (ca. 4000–3500 B.C.), painted pottery gradually displays more and more animal motifs (cases IR-4, 5, 6). Also shown are prehistoric implements including stone hoes, pestles, and mortars. Case IR-6 includes both large and small vessels, one of the former with a frieze showing a row of ibexes and one of the latter with human heads.

IR-7– IR-10 IR-12, 13

The Luristan Bronzes

The bronzes displayed in most of the following cases come from unidentified locations in the mountainous province of Luristan. Although most date from the Iron Age between 1700–500 B.C., recent analyses of the metal reveal that some of the implements go as far back as the late 3rd millennium B.C., contemporary with the Akkadian period in Mesopotamia.

Typical tools and weapons include daggers, axes, and adzes dating from ca. 2300 to 700 B.C. (case IR-7). Many of the types shown are also known from other parts of the ancient Near East.

Among the later bronzes (700–500 B.C.) are tools with animal elements: an adze decorated with a crocodile head, circular axes, and daggers (case IR-8). Shown also are harness elements.

51
52

In case IR-9, horse bits and harness gear decorated with animal elements are displayed. Ibexes, horses, and lions figure prominently.

Personal ornaments include pins, pendants, necklaces and bracelets, plaques, rattle and bell, and figurines (case IR-10). The pins with large disk heads, found with votive objects in the wall of a sanctuary, were used to fasten clothes by piercing the fabric, twisting it into a knot, and then letting the weight of the head keep the knot in place. The pendants are in the shape of animals and other objects, mainly dogs, birds, and ibexes. A silver ring rounds out the collection in this case.

Among the most characteristic items in the repertoire of the Luristan bronzes are the "standards" composed of animals attached to a hollow tube (case IR-12). Thought to have been household fertility symbols, the hollow tubes were probably held erect by inserted branches fastened by a pin. The initial type of "standard" consisted of goat figures with a branch,

48 Dedicatory inscription; glazed bricks.
A 24112
Achaemenid Period
Reign of Xerxes I
486–465 B.C.
Persepolis
Apadana, east wall

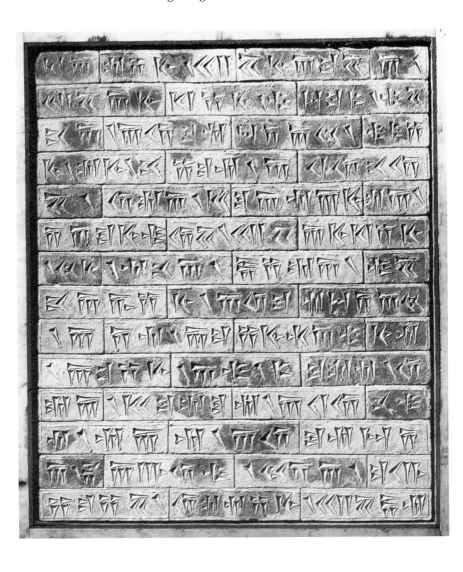

49   Fragment of a human-
headed bull capital; dark
gray limestone.
A 24099
Achaemenid Period
Reign of Darius I
522–485 B.C.
Persepolis
Tripylon

but more elaborate varieties included stylized lions, and a semi-human "hero" attacked by stylized lions.

Luristan bronzes were also used as containers (case IR-13). The bottom shelf contains spouted varieties with both basket and side handles. The middle shelf includes other vessels with pouring spouts, while on the top shelf are typical Tepe Giyan shapes and concave-sided goblets reminiscent of the Mitannian forms. The human-headed goats on one of them may have been to insure good fortune, since such goats were thought to bring luck.

‹-11,
‚ 15

Iron Age Objects from Mazanderan and Northern Iran

Possibly coinciding with the presumed establishment of the Indo-Europeans in northeastern Iran, the earlier painted prehistoric pottery of Tepe Hissar in the Caspian Sea area is replaced in the mid-3rd millennium B.C. by a gray ware style (case IR-11, middle and lower shelves). Tepe Hissar itself was abandoned in the first half of the 2nd millennium B.C., but by the latter part of this millennium, ca. 1350 B.C., the grey style appeared in the Amlash culture south of the Caspian Sea.

The Amlash culture is represented by objects from Mazanderan province southwest of the Caspian Sea (case IR-14). In the early Iron Age after ca. 1350 B.C., a localized assemblage appeared here characterized by animal-shaped vessels, bronze animal and human figurines, swords and lances, and red spouted pottery, as well as the grey ware pottery. Also shown are daggers, swords, and lanceheads dating from ca. 1000–700 B.C.

A wider range of the red and grey wares typical of the Iron Age in the northern area is shown in case IR-15; more of the spouted vessels are seen on the top shelves. On the bottom shelf are vessels from Tepe Giyan level I.

-16–
-34

Achaemenid Remains

Starting on the left of the entrance to the Iranian gallery are remains from the Oriental Institute's excavations at Persepolis, the capital founded by Darius I and intended to be the symbolic capital of the em-

pire, although royal residences are also to be found
at Ecbatana, Susa, Babylon, and Pasargadae. Left to
right:
IR-16. A foundation slab of Xerxes inscribed with Babylonian cuneiform and listing the subject nations under Persian rule shortly after the uprisings that occurred when Xerxes came to the throne. Found in the
garrison quarter at Persepolis.

50   Frieze of striding lions;
dark gray limestone.
A 24068
Achaemenid Period
Reigns of Darius I/Xerxes I
522–465 B.C.
Persepolis
east of the Tochara of
Darius I, from the
balustrade of a small stairway

IR-17. Stairway relief cast from a mold of the original
eastern stairway of the Apadana or Audience Hall.
The Museum's copy of this stairway shows the Lydian
delegation of tribute bearers. The subject peoples sent
delegations that were conducted up these stairs into
the Audience Hall to present their tribute to the king.
Most of these people were represented in a fairly ste-
reotypical manner, with a lock of hair behind the ear

distinguishing the Lydians from the other delegations.

IR-18. The ears of a bull carved in black diorite, from
a column capital.

49   IR-19. A fragment of a human face from a column in
the Tripylon, a three-way gate at the intersection of
promenades leading from the Apadana and the Hall
of a Hundred Columns (the Banquet Hall). The fragment dates to the time of Darius I, 521–486 B.C.

50   IR-20. Next to this is a complete capital in the form
of a bull-man, which probably fitted onto a column,
dating to the reign of Darius I.

IR-21. A relief of rosettes and striding lions, a typical
motif of the period.

51   Mouflon-shaped horse-
bit; bronze.
A 7272
Early first millennium B.C.
Luristan

47

52   Cheek-piece for a
horse-bit in the shape of a
horse; bronze.
A 17321
Early first millennium B.C.
Luristan

IR-22. Directly above this relief is a lintel from a window in the harem (women's quarter) of the palace complex. The molding shows some Egyptian influence.

IR-23. In the center of the back wall facing the entrance to the gallery is a monumental head of a bull, from a pair placed in front of the Hall of a Hundred Columns. The head, which dates to the time of Xerxes, weighs about 10 tons.

IR-24. Several objects made of powdered blue glass in the Egyptian style (reheated and molded) include

an inscribed wall nail, a bowl, and fragments of statues.

IR-25. To the left of the bull is a diorite weight inscribed with a trilingual inscription. Old Persian (the
language of the Achaemenids) and Elamite are on the
broad side, while the same text in Babylonian is on
the narrow side. Found in the Treasury, the weight
dates to the time of Darius I.

IR-26. Immediately in front of the bull is a wall relief
fragment decorated with a rosette design.

IR-27. The reclining feline to the right came from the
entrance of the harem where the king's wives and
children lived. The sculpture dates to the reign of
Xerxes, 485–465 B.C.

IR-28. Next to the reclining feline is a capital in the
form of an Egyptian palm leaf topped by a double
bull (which supported the ceiling beam).

48   Above case IR-14 are inscribed glazed bricks from a
building frieze on the east wall of the Apadana. The
inscription is by Xerxes and commemorates the building additions and modifications that he accomplished
at Persepolis.

IR-29, 30, 31. Free-standing cases contain small finds
left in the ruins after the sack of Persepolis by the
Macedonians under Alexander the Great. In IR-29 are
arrowheads and armor mail plating (scales) and frag-

54   ments of stone vessels, some inscribed with the royal
name. Also exhibited are texts from the Persepolis
archives including examples of Elamite, Aramaic,
Akkadian, Phrygian, and Greek (IR-30). In case IR-31
are several pottery vessels typical of the everyday
ceramics of the period.

53   The Oriental Institute's Achaemenid Gold collection is housed on the right side of the hallway leading
from the Iranian gallery to the Palestinian gallery (IR-
33). Although the precise findspot is unknown, the
ornaments in this treasure are characteristic of the
Achaemenid style and are an outstanding example of
Persian gold working.

Clockwise from top left, the items displayed are:
1) griffin heads probably meant to be attached to a
fabric; 2) a row of matched roaring lion heads facing
both left and right, probably originally attached to
fabric heads facing symmetrically toward each other;
3) roundels with paired snarling lions in repoussé,
again probably attached to a fabric; 4) striding lions
with details made of gold wire; 5) a long row of strid-

53 The "Chicago Persian
    Treasure"; gold.
    A 28581–88
    Achaemenid Period
    Reign of Artaxerxes II
    404–359 B.C.
    probably from Ecbatana

ing lions: these cut-outs were probably attached by the loops in the lions' tails; 6) a small ram head; 7) a very elaborate necklace with miniature horned lion heads; 8) a small roundel with an encircled figure of the Persian god Ahuramazda holding a plant and dressed in a typical Persian style; 9) in the center is a roundel with a winged lion in a snarling posture with turned head—this roundel is the largest of its kind known.

In case IR-32, to the right of the Achaemenid Gold collection, a fragment of a stone lion head from Persepolis is displayed. It was originally part of a double lion capital.

In case IR-34, to the left of the gold, is a limestone trial piece. Even though this model was found in Egypt, the motifs represented on it reveal the Achaemenid style.

54 Fragments of fine royal vessels which were deliberately smashed by the soldiers of Alexander the Great during the destruction of the Achaemenid capital in 330 B.C.; stone.
Achaemenid Period
Reigns of Darius I–Darius III
about 522–330 B.C.
Persepolis

Palestine

THE NAME PALESTINE refers to the geographical area
that comprises most of what is now Israel and Jordan.
Derived from the name of the Philistines, the name
first was used by the Romans to designate a province
of the empire, and subsequently through usage
under both Byzantine and Islamic rule it became part
of our vocabulary under the British occupation after
World War I. Midway between East and West, Palestine—also the home of the Biblical traditions—is a
sliver of land sandwiched between vast expanses of
desert and sea. Vast, that is, in terms of the time,
expense, and danger involved in crossing this formidable landscape in the fragile ships and cumber-
some caravans of ancient times; and, consequently,
vast in the tremendous cultural gulf that existed between ancient Palestine and its neighbors to the east
and west. Yet, for all its diminutive stature and iso-
lation, Palestine was neither homogeneous nor a
backwater. The topography of Palestine is a diverse
blend of Mediterranean inlets, stretches of gravelly
deserts, green valleys and rolling pastures,
sculptured canyons of red sandstone, and rugged
limestone hills covered with pine and scrubby oak.
And through it all, a thin strip of water: the fresh-
water Sea of Galilee in the north, the salty Dead Sea
in the south, and, connecting the two, the winding
Jordan River. It is against this backdrop of diversity
that there emerged a series of cultures, uniquely Palestinian in nature, which ultimately were to foster
the three great monotheistic religions of our times,
Judaism, Christianity, and Islam.

To a large extent, the history of this land is rooted
in its peculiar geography. The combination of diversity in terrain and compactness in size gave rise to
relatively inconsequential political powers and cultures that seldom achieved originality in civilization.
Kingdoms, principalities, and sheikhdoms were
large in pomp and ambition, but rare were the times
when great leaders were able to surmount the petti-
ness of local lords. Diversity resulted, too, in a culture that was prone to adopt and assimilate all that

HISTORICAL
VIEW

was foreign—of good taste or bad—while often re-
casting that which was alien into a refreshingly new
mold. At times boldly volatile, but more often than
not restrained and conservative, Palestine traced a
history and culture that were never uninteresting.

The stamp of this historical course was set well
before writing appeared. Shortly after the end of the
last Ice Age, for instance, there existed in Natufian
times (10,000–8000 B.C.) a flourishing artistic skill in
carving bone for both utilitarian and decorative purposes. Slightly later, in the Pre-Pottery Neolithic
period (8000–6000 B.C.), a large settlement at Jericho,
near the Dead Sea, was fortified by an impressive
stone wall and round tower. This is the earliest
example of monumental architecture in the region.
Burials found in this settlement took an elaborate
form: groups of skulls were found separated from the
rest of the skeletons, with plaster and shells adorning
the skulls to produce a macabre mask-like effect. Yet,
despite this early leap in cultural achievement, the
next 2000 years (Late Neolithic, 6000–4000 B.C.) saw
no significant progress in the lifestyles, if not in the
economic development, of these early farming villages. Not until the centuries around 3000 B.C. is
there a dramatic, almost abrupt entrance onto the
wide stage of intense international relations and
urban civilizations then emerging throughout the
Near East.

Prefaced only by subtle signs in the Chalcolithic
period (4000–3000 B.C.)—the appearance of new,
elaborate ritual objects, the introduction of copperworking, advancements in farming and herding, and
sporadic examples of mural painting and ivory
carving—the sudden burst of activity in the Early
Bronze Age (3000–2000 B.C.) was centered around
the emergence of a web of fortified city-states. No
examples of writing have come down to us from this
early period to provide even hints of the ethnic
makeup of the local population, although the splendid royal archives recently found at Ebla shed a
shadowy light on what were probably kingdoms of
Semitic-speaking peoples. Archaeological remains,
therefore, remain our only source of enlightenment
on the birth of cities.

One characteristic of these city-states that immediately draws our attention is their compact
area—often less than twenty acres, or about two of

Chicago's standard city blocks. But within the thick, often elaborate defensive walls surrounding each city, an amazingly sophisticated and cosmopolitan layout is to be found. Religious edifices like temples, public buildings, and closely packed domestic quarters with closed drains meet the eye. These endow the early cities with an image of patterned chaos, an orderliness that some believe to have been influenced by the inhabitants' conception of the world. Less prepossessing, but nevertheless a characteristic feature of daily life, are the beginnings of a fairly standardized repertoire of pottery vessels, the most prominent of which were jars and pitchers that contained the principal products of the land, oil and wine. A feature of this period, too, is the group burials, often in caves or shaft graves, which with their offerings of pottery vessels (probably containing food for the dead) may have been the ancient version of the family vault.

Hand in hand with the appearance of the city-states was the growth of international relations between Palestine and the ancient world, a pattern of war and trade which was to last throughout its history. Both the archaeological and written records provide a rich account of the interchanges that ultimately spread as far as the Aegean civilization and Mediterranean world to the west, the Arabian peninsula and Indian Ocean southward, and Mesopotamia and eventually China to the east. Egypt, however, was ever the major partner and covetous neighbor in these exchanges. Although strong Egyptian contact, and perhaps conquest, is seen, for instance, as early as 3000 B.C. (numerous Egyptian objects including two inscriptions with the name of one of the first Egyptian pharaohs appear in Palestine), the vital link between Palestine and her neighbors becomes particularly prominent in the Middle and Late Bronze Ages (2000–1550 and 1550–1200 B.C.). The Egyptian side of the balance is most often found in their texts, tombs, and reliefs. Timber, wine, and resin were some of the attractions that drew them to Palestine, but more of a mixed blessing was the influx of illegal and legal aliens into Egypt. While the Egyptians frequently depicted Palestinian captives in their reliefs, less desirable were the incursions of Asiatics reflected in the Beni Hasan tomb paintings, the Biblical story of Joseph, and the people known as the Hyksos. On the Palestinian side of the ledger, exotic luxury items of gold and alabaster, and statuettes and scarabs were imported; but far more important was the borrowing of ideas in religion, literature, and art. Biblical wisdom literature, for instance, had its origins in Egypt. A sense of just how deeply embroiled the Canaanite world was in international politics may be perceived in the eclectic motifs of ivory carvings, the importation of Mycenaean and Cypriot pottery from the Mediterranean world, cylinder seals from Mesopotamia, and, not least, the introduction of cuneiform writing as in the letters written by Palestinian princes found at Amarna in Egypt. As autonomous kingdoms (in the Middle Bronze Age) or as subjugated provinces under the Egyptian New Kingdom (during the Late Bronze Age), the Semitic city-states of Palestine were not a land bridge nor a crossroads, but neither were they isolated.

The enduring cycle of local independence and imperial province is repeated in the Iron Age (1200–332 B.C.), when the region became first centralized under the Israelite kingdom, then fragmented into two rival kingdoms (Israel and Judah), and finally conquered by the Assyrians, Babylonians, and Persians in turn. Perhaps best known as the age in which the sources of the Old Testament crystallized, it is also the period in which the Canaanite alphabet, one of the major cultural contributions of the region, evolved into the Phoenician, Hebrew, Aramaic, and Greek. The widespread use of this revolutionary writing system democratized forever the ability to read and write and to keep accounts and records. With the collapse of the Canaanite city-states at the end of the Bronze Age, the kings of Israel and Judah established new capitals at Samaria and Jerusalem, and converted the Canaanite cities into new fortresses and storehouses. The Oriental Institute excavations at Megiddo—the biblical Armageddon—best illustrate how vestiges of its Canaanite past merged with the new order to produce a drab but nevertheless original material culture. Well planned cities like Beersheva with a number of new architectural elements, the forging of iron implements, and the new settling and farming of terraced plots in the hill country were superimposed, not without difficulty, on a Canaanite past. On the other hand, the presence of Greek pottery, Phoenician ivories, and Assyrian "Palace" pottery, and the importation of spices from Arabia, reflect the new web of international links with a wider world and its merger with local innovations.

Palestinian history, of course, does not end with the fall of Jerusalem in 586 B.C. or even the conquest by Alexander the Great in 331 B.C. What follows in the Hellenistic (332–63 B.C.), Roman (63 B.C.–324 A.D.), Byzantine (324–640 A.D.), and Islamic (630–present) periods is certainly as important as what went before. From the foundations of Christianity to the establishment of the Islamic faith, this subsequent history is a kaleidoscope of continued involvement, within first the western Greco-Roman world and then the eastern Islamic world. Except for a brief moment of local rule under the Umayyad Caliphs (661–750 A.D.), for instance, the entire Islamic period is one of subjugation by conquerors from Egypt, Iraq, and Turkey. Yet, despite and perhaps because of this, the art and architecture as well as the articles of daily life from the more recent ages equal or even surpass those of earlier, Biblical times in artistic and technical sophistication.

The Islamic Period

HISTORICAL VIEW

The Islamic era starts in 622 A.D., with the prophet Muhammad's flight from Mecca to Medina. With the rise of Islam and the unification of Arabia, the Islamic faith swiftly spread throughout much of the known world, from the shores of the Atlantic across the Near East to India and the frontiers of China. Alien cultures and traditions were absorbed and a new unity achieved, through the common belief in Muhammad as the Prophet of God, with Islam manifest in the text of the Holy Qur'an. With the rise and fall of dynasties and the shift of power from one center to another, the single constant is this unity of belief. Two of its fundamental tenets were prayer and pilgrimage to Mecca.

The mosque form evolved to cater to the spiritual needs of the faithful, providing a space large enough to accommodate the congregation and indicating the direction of Mecca to the worshippers. In Syria, under the Umayyads (632–750 A.D.), a number of early mosques were converted from churches but the Great Mosque in Damascus and the Dome of the Rock in Jerusalem were both original Umayyad constructions. So were a number of palaces and hunting lodges in the Syrian and Jordanian desert.

Under the Abbasids (750–1258 A.D.) the capital was moved to Baghdad; the Umayyads fled to Spain to establish Islam in the heart of Western Europe. Moving westward from Central Asia, the Seljuks, and later the Mongols, modified the Islamic state and brought changes to the life of conquerors and conquered alike. In Egypt, the Fatimids and the Mamluks represent two peaks in the cultural achievement of Islam. In Persia the Safavids, and in India the Mughals are noted for comparable artistic eminence. Trade was vigorously pursued throughout the Islamic world, both overland and by sea; the consequence was a prosperity in which the arts flourished, with unparalleled developments in architecture and the fine arts, ceramics, textiles, glass, and metalwork.

With the invasion of Turkey by the Ottomans in the fourteenth century and the capture of Constantinople in 1453 A.D., the last great empire in the Middle East was forged. Much of the Near East and North Africa fell to the Turks; their culture reached its zenith in the sixteenth century. With the rise of Western Europe, the Turkish empire declined, until it was finally dismembered after the First World War.

GALLERY PLAN

Palestine

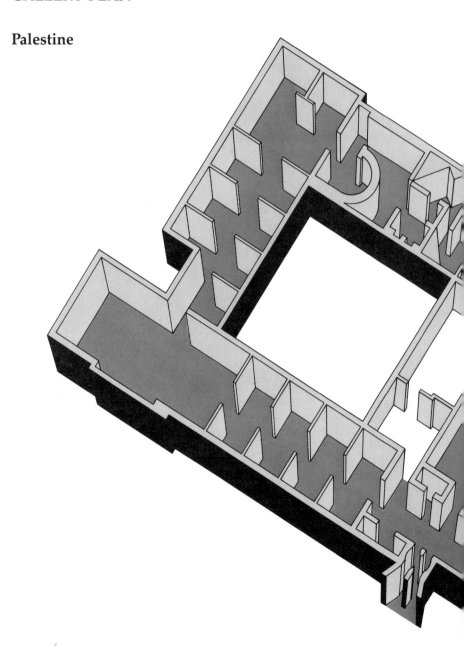

GALLERY EXHIBITS

Palestine

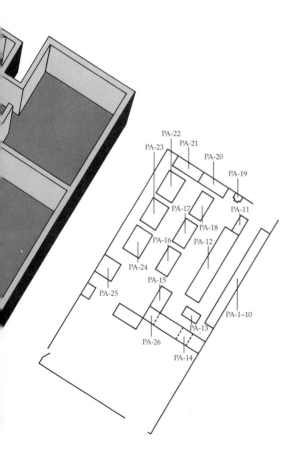

1–
10

On the left entering the gallery

The *Chronology of Palestinian Pottery* is the basic tool by which archaeologists date their excavations. The timespan represented here extends from the earliest handmade pottery (Neolithic period, ca. 5000 B.C.) to the Roman period in the first centuries A.D. Widespread wheelmade pottery (notice the wheelmarks on the necks and bases particularly) begins in the Middle Bronze (MB) Age (PA-4, 5) at the peak of the Canaanite city-states (and the Hyksos). Painting becomes a more frequent decoration in the Late Bronze (LB) Age (PA-5, 6, 7). Note also the evolution of oil lamps from a simple dish in Early Bronze (EB) (PA-2) to a pinched-spout vessel in LB II (PA-5), and the development of cooking pots from Iron II (PA-9) to the Roman period (PA-10) (antecedents not shown here go back to the Middle Bronze Age). Foreign relations are seen in: 1) the Cypriot influence and imports in MB II, LB, and Iron II; 2) Mycenaean imports in the LB; 3) "Philistine" pottery in Iron I (similar to late Mycenaean pottery), perhaps the finest ware ever made in the area; and 4) Nabatean painted pottery from Jordan in Roman times.

11
12

55

On the right

Case PA-11 contains imports into Palestine from the 2nd millennium B.C.

The Bab edh-Dhra shaft tomb and charnel house displayed in case PA-12 are from the largest ancient cemetery site ever discovered in Jordan. The tomb furnishings and customs of the Early Bronze Age are well illustrated in this exhibit; group burials with pottery offerings were typical. The vessels in the exhibit can be compared with those from the EB in the pottery chronology display.

55 Selected pottery from a shaft tomb and a charnel house.
O.I. 1978.2.1–198
shaft tomb, Early Bronze Age I
charnel house, Early Bronze Age III
3rd millennium B.C.
Jordan
Bab edh-Dhra

13–
15

57

58

Religious Life

Just beyond the Bab edh-Dhra tomb are objects relating to *Religious Life:* in case PA-13, a Jewish ossuary that contained the bones of the deceased with a Hebrew inscription, "Yo'ezer, son of Yehoḥanan, the scribe" (this one dates to the Roman period); in case PA-14, a "horned" altar such as is often mentioned in the Bible (Ex. 27:1), and a principal feature of Israelite sanctuaries; in case PA-15, a fragment of a Dead

56 Proto-Aeolic capital;
limestone.
A 13394
Iron Age II A
10th century B.C.
Megiddo
Stratum V A/IV B

57 Horned Altar;
limestone.
A 13201
Iron Age II A
10th century B.C.
Megiddo
Stratum V A/IV B

123

58 Fragment of a scroll
from a non-Biblical Essene
Psalter, inscribed in
Hebrew on both sides;
parchment.
A 30303
1st century A.D.
Palestine
Qumran Cave 4

59 Pottery jar and
parchment fragment from
the Dead Sea Scrolls.
A 29304 a, b
A 30303
1st century A.D.
Palestine
Qumran Caves

59

Sea Scroll and its container jar found in a cave at Qumran in the barren Judean desert overlooking the Dead Sea (dating to the early Roman period).

Megiddo

PA-16–
PA-18

In the center of the gallery, we come to three cases (PA-16, 17, 18) containing the *Megiddo Ivories,* one of the largest and finest collections of Canaanite and Phoenician art. Excavated from the LB and Iron Age levels at Megiddo, most of them come from a semi-subterranean chamber called the "treasury," within a large building or palace at the site (see wall exhibit). The ivories include furniture inlays (66), cosmetic vessels (81, 82), combs (56, 83), a game board and gaming pieces (19–22), miniatures (48–51), and plaques (14–18, 57, 58, 61). In addition to Canaanite motifs (38–52), many display Egyptian (70, 71), Aegean (56–58), Assyrian (59, 60), or Hittite (61) motifs and influences.

8
61

60

At the end of the gallery, next to the entrance, is a capital of a pilaster (engaged column) found at Iron Age (Israelite) Megiddo (PA-19). Made in the "Proto-Aeolic" style, which derives from an Egyptian plant, it is a direct forebear of the later Greek Aeolian and perhaps Ionic capitals.

PA-19
56

On the back wall beside the capital is grouped material relating to the architecture of the "Solomonic" era, of the latter half of the 10th century B.C.

60 Griffin plaque, designed according to the Mycenaean style; ivory.
A 22212
Late Bronze Age II
13th century B.C.
Megiddo
Treasury, near the palace

61　A selection of female
heads from the Megiddo
Ivories.

A 22263–66, A 22276
Late Bronze Age II
13th century B.C.

Megiddo
Treasury, near the palace

On the window side

A22–
A-25

On the window side of the gallery are three cases, PA-22–24. In the first case, PA-22, is a collection of the kind of objects taken as booty from Megiddo and neighboring regions by Thutmosis III and his army during his campaign there in 1484 B.C. In the second case, PA-23, the central display contains objects generally associated with *Cultic Rituals*. The actual function of these zoomorphic figurines (some may be toys), "wall brackets," and the votive kernos vessel are unknown. In the third case, PA-24, are bronze figurines of presumed *Canaanite Gods*. These are typical of the cultic objects in the 2nd millennium B.C.

62 Canaanite gods; bronze.
A 18331
A 24637
A 18630
A 27212
A 18355
Middle Bronze Age II–Early Iron Age
about 1750–1150 B.C.
Syria-Palestine

63 Upper part of a statuette of a mother goddess; terracotta.
A 19191
Iron Age II about 800 B.C.
Megiddo

The pottery figurines are mostly of the Iron Age and shed light on a hidden aspect of Israelite daily life, the continuation of an indigenous Canaanite religion. Of Egyptian origin are the alabaster vessels and fragments of statuary from the 2nd millennium B.C. The considerably later Aramaic incantation bowl from Nippur, inscribed with Biblical passages to ward off female demons, is an artifact of the deportation of Judeans to Babylonia.

Halfway down the gallery on the window side is case PA-25, a display of the major objects used in *Religious Activities* of the Canaanite city-states: a large model shrine, and two offering stands or incense burners. Although they are found generally in temple deposits, their precise function is unknown.

64

64 Objects from the Me-
giddo Cult: a shrine and an
offering stand; terracotta.

A 18308—shrine
Late Bronze Age I
about 1300 B.C.

A 20830—offering stand
Early Iron Age I
about 1150 B.C.

Islamic Materials

PA-26

A selection from the Oriental Institute's collection of Islamic material is usually on display in the Palestinian gallery. The Institute possesses a remarkable fragment of the *Thousand and One Nights* story (PA-26). It is the title page and beginning of the Arabian Nights, and was written in Arabic before 879 A.D., when the fragment was used as scrap paper by a legal scribe. It is the oldest dated example of a *paper* book in the Western world.

Also in the collection is a comprehensive group of medieval Islamic bookbindings and covers, mostly of the Mamluk dynasty; Arabic, Persian, and Turkish manuscripts, Qur'ans, and *firmans*; and numerous Arabic papyri, all of which once belonged to the famous German Orientalist, Dr. Bernhard Moritz. They were acquired from him by James Henry Breasted in 1929, along with a heterogeneous collection of Near Eastern antiquities.

Other Islamic material includes early Islamic pottery and glass from the Institute's excavations at Istakhr and Rayy, in Iran; a number of objects from Fustat, old Cairo; a magnificent Persian calligrapher's manual with lacquer covers, assembled in the 19th century from earlier 15th and 18th century pages; a fine astrolabe, engraved by the Persian craftsman Abd al-A'imma (1668–1720 A.D.); and a Persian lacquer box painted with flowers and birds and inscribed with verses by the famous poet Qa'ani (1808–1854 A.D.) (PA-26).

65

66

Finally, the Museum possesses a superb collection of Palestinian and Near Eastern costumes and jewelry donated in 1981 by Clara Struve Klingeman.

65   An astrolabe, engraved by Abd al-A'imma (1668–1720 A.D.)
A 4091
17th century
Persia

66   A Persian lacquer box, inscribed with verses by the Qajar poet Qa'ani (1808–1852 A.D.)
A 30805
19th century
Persia

	EGYPT	PALESTINE	SYRIA	ANATOLIA	CYPRUS & THE AEGEAN	MESOPOTAMIA	IRAN
		Kebaran				Shanidar Cave	
						Zarzi	
						Palegawra	
9000 B.C.							
		Natufian				Karim Shahir	
						Malefaat	
						Zawi Chemi	
8000 B.C.							
7000 B.C.		Pre-Pottery Neolithic / Jericho		Neolithic	Cyprus Aegean		Ali Kosh
				Çayönü	Pre-Pottery Neolithic / Jarmo		
6000 B.C.		Pottery Neolithic	Amuq A B · C	Chatal Hüyük	Neolithic	Hassuna	Archaic Susiana Chogha Mish
	Badarian					Samarra	
5000 B.C.					Pottery Neolithic		

Comparative chronological chart of the ancient Near East and eastern Mediterranean. Time scale (left axis): 4000 B.C., 3000 B.C., 2000 B.C., 1000 B.C., B.C./A.D., 1000 A.D. Central band markers: E, F, G, H, I, J, K.

Date	Egypt / Nubia	Palestine (E–K)	Syria (J)	Mesopotamia	Anatolia	Cyprus	Aegean / Greece	Elam / Iran
4000 B.C.	Amratian = Naqada I; Nubian A Group	Chalcolithic	Chalcolithic	Ubaid	Chalcolithic			
	Gerzean = Naqada II–III; Archaic	Early Bronze	Early Bronze	Uruk = Protoliterate A–B				Proto-Elamite
3000 B.C.	Early Bronze			Jemdet Nasr = Protoliterate C–D	Early Bronze		Early Helladic	Susa
	Archaic			Early Dynastic; Sumerians		Early Cypriot	Middle Helladic	
	Old Kingdom; Nubian C Group			Akkadian				
				Ur III; Gutians				
2000 B.C.	First Intermediate	Early Bronze IV / Middle Bronze I	Ebla Kingdom	Isin/Larsa; Old Assyrian		Middle Cypriot	Minoan (Crete)	Early Elamite
	Middle Kingdom	Middle Bronze	Mari; Alalakh	Hammurabi; Old Babylonian	Hittite Old Kingdom			
	Second Intermediate (Hyksos)	Hyksos		Mitanni (Hurrians); Kassite		Late Cypriot	Mycenaean	
	New Kingdom	Late Bronze	Late Bronze; Ugarit	Middle Assyrian	Hittite Empire	Cypro-Geometric	Proto-Geometric	Middle Elamite
1000 B.C.		Iron Age; Kingdom of David & Solomon	Iron Age	Neo-Assyrian	Iron Age	Cypro-Archaic	Geometric; Archaic	
	Third Intermediate	Fall of Samaria; Fall of Jerusalem; Babylonian Exile		Neo-Babylonian	Lydian Kingdom; Urartu; Manneans	Cypro-Classical	Classical	
	Cushite & Saite Dynasties; Meroitic Nubia; Persians	Persians	Persians	Persians	Persians			Persians
	Alexander the Great; Ptolemies	Alexander the Great; Hasmoneans	Alexander the Great; Antigonid & Seleucid Kings	Alexander the Great; Seleucid Kings	Alexander the Great	Alexander the Great	Alexander the Great; Hellenistic Kingdoms	Alexander the Great
B.C.		Seleucid Kings						
A.D.	Roman Period	Roman Period	Roman Period	Parthians	Roman Period		Roman Period	Parthians
	Coptic Period	Byzantine Empire	Byzantine Empire	Sassanians	Byzantine Empire		Byzantine Empire	Sassanians
1000 A.D.	Arab Caliphates	Arab Caliphates	Arab Caliphates	Arab Caliphates	Arab Caliphates		Byzantine Empire; Arab Caliphates	Arab Caliphates

67 The *Islamic Bindings and Bookmaking* exhibition, 1981.

Special Exhibitions

Part of the Palestinian Gallery is reserved for special exhibits, either for material from the Institute's reserve collections or for exhibitions from other institutions. Since 1977 when a special exhibition on *The Magic of Egyptian Art* was held in conjunction with *The Treasures of Tutankhamun* exhibition at the Field Museum, a number of other exhibits on a broad range of topics have been displayed. These include *A Photographer's World,* a collection of photographs of Germany in the 1930's by Ursula Schneider, late photographer at the Oriental Institute; *Artists in Egypt, 1920–1935,* explaining the work of the Epigraphic Survey and the methods used to record material, illustrated by the original drawings and paintings made on the spot; *From a Syrian Suq,* a highly popular reconstruction of a Syrian market, with actual goods for sale in the shops; *Excavations from Carthage, Then and Now,* a history of archaeological exploration at ancient Carthage, highlighting the Oriental Institute's recent participation in the international archaeological salvage program; *Near Eastern Costumes from the Klingeman Collection,* a magnificent collection of Near Eastern dresses and jewelry recently donated to the Institute; *The Photographs of Bonfils 1867–1907: Remembrances of the Near East,* a collection of early photographs of the area; *Alexander in the East,* a selection of objects of the time of Alexander the Great, to coincide with the *Alexander* exhibition at the Art Institute of Chicago; and *Islamic Bindings and Bookmaking,* an exhibition of the Institute's own collection of medieval Islamic bindings. Further exhibitions are planned to draw attention to the Museum's permanent collection and to demonstrate the research work of the Oriental Institute, such as *Publishing the Past,* a survey of academic publications by Institute scholars during the past ten years.

67

68 Oriental Institute Members' Tour at the Tutankhamun Colonnade with the staff of our Epigraphic Survey, Luxor Temple.

Oriental Institute Membership

The Oriental Institute has a large and active membership program. Contributions from this program are used to support the Museum as well as the Institute's research and archaeological field projects. Members receive a monthly newsletter featuring articles on current research, the Institute's history, and new exhibits and publications; letters from field excavations; and notices of lectures, courses, tours, and other events. Members also receive the Oriental Institute's Annual Report, which contains detailed accounts of progress in the year's research, excavations, museum exhibits, publications, and other programs.

There is an extensive lecture program, a Members' Day featuring tours behind the scenes at the Institute, and a reduced rate on weekend courses offered on various aspects of Near Eastern archaeology, history, language, and culture. Many members participate in the Volunteer Program which offers tours of the Museum, helps to staff the Museum store, and assists with some of the comprehensive educational programs for children.

The Oriental Institute sponsors archaeological tours for members to the Near East and Europe and members may visit Institute excavations in the field (subject to prior arrangement and the limitations imposed by the field director). Members also receive a discount in the Institute's Museum store, The Suq.

*Please address
all inquiries to:*

The Membership Secretary
The Oriental Institute
The University of Chicago
1155 East 58th Street
Chicago, Illinois 60637

Telephone: (312) 753-2389

Memberships are on a yearly basis and may be in the name of both husband and wife. Contributions are deductible for income tax purposes.

Annual membership $20.00
Foreign annual membership $25.00
Sustaining membership $50.00
Associate membership $100.00
Contributing membership $500.00
Sponsor $1000.00

Ancient Near East